S.T.(P) Technology Today
A Series for Technicians

Engineering Science Level II

S.T.(P) Technology Today
A Series for Technicians

Engineering Science Level II

G D Redford
CEng MIMechE MIProdE MIED
Senior Lecturer, Mechanical and Production
Engineering Department, Wigan College of Technology

D T Rees
BSc CEng MIEE
Dean of Faculty of Science & Technology,
Gwent College of Higher Education, Newport, Gwent

A Greer
CEng MRAeS
Formerly Senior Lecturer, Gloucester City College of
Technology

Stanley Thornes (Publishers) Ltd.

First published in 1982 by:
Stanley Thornes (Publishers) Ltd
EDUCA House
Old Station Drive
off Leckhampton Road
CHELTENHAM GL53 0DN
England

British Library Cataloguing in Publication Data

Redford, G.D.
    Engineering Science
    Level II.
    1. Engineering
    I. Title   II. Rees, D.T.   III. Greer, A.
    620   TA145

    ISBN 0-85950-313-5

Typeset by TECH-SET, Unit 3, Brewery Lane, Felling, Tyne & Wear
Printed and bound in Great Britain by
Ebenezer Baylis & Son Limited
The Trinity Press, Worcester, and London

CONTENTS

PREFACE

Engineering Science Level II follows on naturally from our earlier book *Engineering and Physical Science Level I*. The new book has been written to meet the needs of technicians following the TEC standard unit on the A5 programme, and it will also be found to meet nearly all the requirements of students taking the half-units on the A1 programme.

The objectives covered have been listed at the head of each chapter and, as in the previous book, the text is supported with numerous worked examples and exercises.

G D Redford
D T Rees
A Greer
1982

ACKNOWLEDGEMENTS

The authors and publishers are grateful to the following for permission to reproduce previously published material:

Mr J G Kelly AIIP, for various line diagrams and photographs

Scopex Instruments Ltd, for Fig. 5.1

Gould Instruments Ltd, for Fig. 5.10

Longman Group Ltd, for permission to use material from *The Cathode Ray Oscilloscope* by David T Rees

Siemens Ltd, for Fig. 3.13

Central Electricity Generating Board, for Figs. 4.9 and 4.10.

Electronic Brokers Ltd, for Fig. 2.16

Wessex Electronics Ltd, for Fig. 2.17

Electrical Review, for the chart (Fig. A9): 'Electric Shock: Act at once, delay is fatal'. (Enquiries about purchasing the chart, which is available in paper, card or plastic, to General Sales Manager, IPC Electrical-Electronic Press Ltd, Quadrant House, The Quadrant, Sutton, Surrey, SM2 5AS. Tel: 01-661 3500.)

ELECTRICAL CIRCUITS

After reaching the end of this chapter you should be able to:

1. *Define current as the rate of movement of charge.*
2. *Define the coulomb as 1 ampere second.*
3. *Define potential difference in terms of energy per coulomb.*
4. *Define electromotive force in terms of the total energy per coulomb produced by the source.*
5. *Define internal resistance as the resistance offered by the source to the flow of current.*
6. *Define terminal potential difference as the voltage between the source terminals (and across the external circuit) when a current is flowing.*
7. *Solve problems involving a d.c. source with internal resistance.*

CIRCUIT DIAGRAMS

An electrical circuit consisting of a battery, bulb and switch is shown in Fig. 1.1. The parts are connected by wires, usually made of copper, which is assumed to have negligible resistance. The circuit can be represented by a circuit diagram (Fig. 1.2) which uses standard graphical symbols to represent each component of the circuit. A table of standard symbols is shown in Fig. 1.3.

A basic electrical circuit, showing a resistor connected to a battery would, using these symbols, appear as in Fig. 1.4.

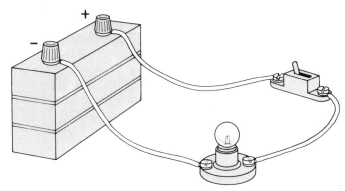

Fig. 1.1   Real-life circuit

1

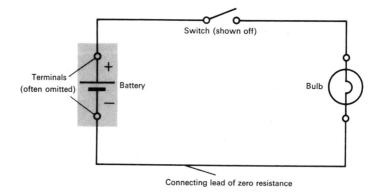

Switch (shown off)

Terminals
(often omitted)

+

Battery

−

Bulb

Connecting lead of zero resistance

Fig. 1.2 Circuit diagram of Fig. 1.1

The battery voltage and the voltage across the resistor are indicated by E and V respectively in association with + and − signs, and the current represented by the arrow and symbol I. Other symbols used for electrical quantities are given in Table 1.1.

TABLE 1.1
Electrical Quantities and Their Symbols

Quantity	Symbol	Unit	Symbol
Voltage	E or V	volt	V
Current	I	ampere	A
Resistance	R	ohm	Ω
Charge	Q	coulomb	C
Energy	E or W	joule	J
Power	P	watt	W
Time	t	second	s

It is useful to think of circuit diagrams as representing the flow of power from left to right (Fig. 1.5). Thus the battery is a *source* or *input* of power and the heat produced in the resistor the *output*. When circuit diagrams are drawn in this way you should acquire the habit of 'reading' them from left to right.

Sometimes it may be more appropriate to consider the output as current or voltage or even a magnetic field if a magnetic circuit is involved.

Component	Symbols	Notes
Conductor, wire or lead		Implies zero resistance
Crossing wires	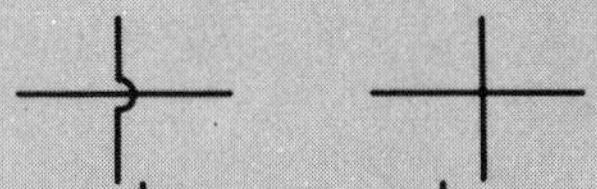	No electrical connection between wires
Junction of two or more conductors	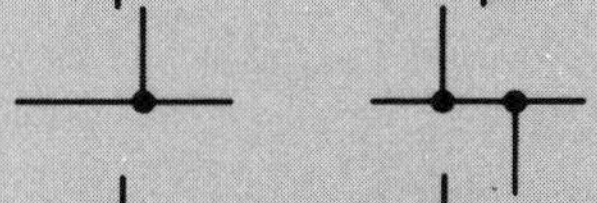	
Earth connection		Second symbol also used for connection to metal case
Switch (single way and two way)		Called 'single pole' since it 'breaks' only one conductor
Battery (one cell and multi cell)	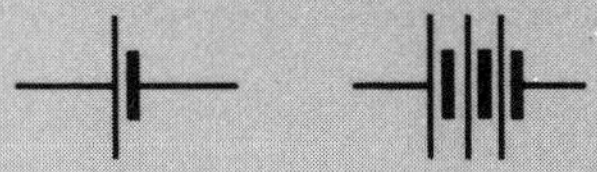	Positive terminal is longer line. Either symbol is also used for any d.c. source
Resistor	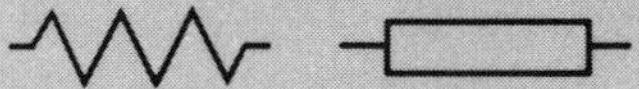	
Variable resistor	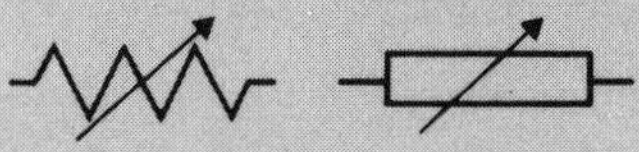	
Potential or voltage divider	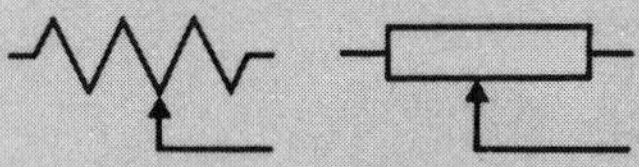	May also be used as a symbol for a variable resistor
Alternative method of showing voltage divider	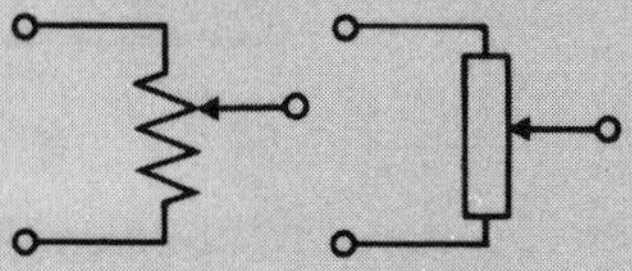	Often referred to as a 'pot'
Capacitor	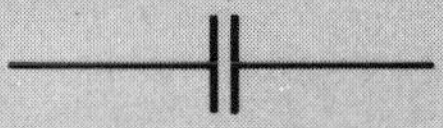	
Inductor (coil)	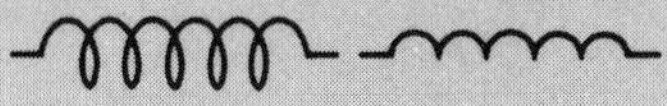	
Diode or Rectifier		Arrow indicates 'easy' direction of current flow
Bulb (lamp)	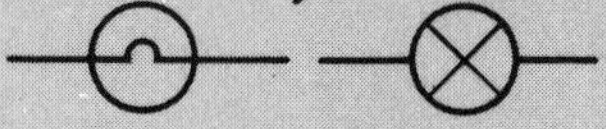	Second symbol is used for indicator lamps
Fuse link		Rating is usually shown by a number
Voltmeter and Ammeter	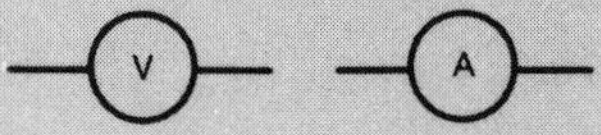	For millivoltmeter and milliammeter letters mV and mA are used

Fig. 1.3 Symbols for electrical components

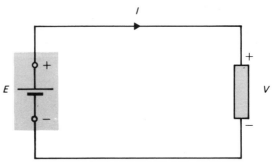

Fig. 1.4   Basic circuit

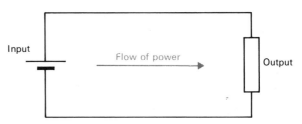

Fig. 1.5   Direction of power flow

CURRENT, VOLTAGE AND RESISTANCE

CURRENT

In the circuit of Fig. 1.1, if the switch is closed, an electric current will flow through the circuit. This current is a *flow of electrons*. As the electrons pass through the bulb filament heat will be generated. If the heat is sufficient, the bulb filament will reach a temperature at which it emits light.

Electrons are negatively charged particles, and therefore *a current may be defined as a flow of electric charge* (symbol Q). Electrical charge is measured in *coulombs* (symbol C), and if one coulomb per second flows in a wire the current is said to be one *ampere* (A) (Fig. 1.6). That is,

$$1 \text{ ampere} = 1 \text{ coulomb per second}$$

$$I = \frac{Q}{t} \qquad\qquad [1.1]$$

It is of interest to note that one electron carries a charge of only 1.6×10^{-19} C, so there are 6.25×10^{18} electrons in every coulomb.

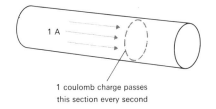 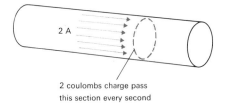

1 coulomb charge passes this section every second   2 coulombs charge pass this section every second

Fig. 1.6   Current is the rate of flow of charge

From the above it can be seen that the charge flowing past a point in a circuit is given by

$$\text{Charge} = \text{Current} \times \text{Time}$$
$$\text{or} \quad Q = It \qquad\qquad [1.2]$$

It should be noted that the convention used for current is that it flows out of the positive terminal of the battery (Fig. 1.4). This convention was adopted before the discovery of the electron when it was thought that electric current was a flow of *positive* charge. Now we know it is the flow of electrons, which are *negative* charge carriers, and so the 'real' current made up of electron flow is in the opposite direction to that indicated. However, we have decided to live with the mistake our forefathers made, and there is no harm in thinking for this work that current is a flow of positive charge.

WORKED EXAMPLE 1

A current of 0.3 A flows through a bulb for 10 s. Calculate: (a) the total charge transferred through the bulb, (b) the number of electrons that have passed through.

SOLUTION

(a)   Since   Charge = Current × Time   (equation [1.2])

          $Q = 0.3\,\text{A} \times 10\,\text{s} = 3\,\text{C}$

(b)   Since $1\,\text{C} = 6.25 \times 10^{18}$

          Number of electrons in 3 C $= 3 \times 6.25 \times 10^{18} = 18.75 \times 10^{18}$

WORKED EXAMPLE 2

Fig. 1.7 shows current against time for two different circuits. In which circuit is the transfer of charge greatest over the first 30 seconds?

SOLUTION

For circuit 1   Charge $= 2\,\text{A} \times 30\,\text{s} = 60\,\text{C}$

For circuit 2   Charge for first $20\,s = \frac{1}{2}\,A \times 20\,s = 10\,C$

Charge over next $10\,s = 2\frac{1}{2}\,A \times 10\,s = 25\,C$

Total charge transferred $= 10 + 25 = 35\,C$

Circuit 1 transfers the greatest charge over $30\,s$.

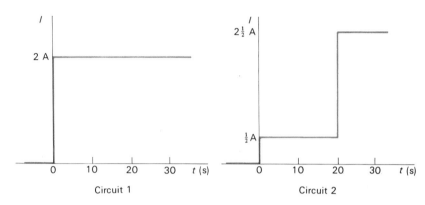

Fig. 1.7   Information for Worked Example 2

It can be seen from the above that the charge transferred is equal to the area under the current–time curve. This fact can be used to calculate the total charge in cases where the current is not constant.

VOLTAGE

The energy to move electrons around the circuit is provided by the battery. The fact that the battery possesses energy is evident by the existence of a voltage across its terminals. This can be shown by connecting a voltmeter across the terminals, and for the type of battery shown the voltmeter would read $4\frac{1}{2}$ V, say. If this was so, to move a total charge of 1 coulomb around the circuit would use up $4\frac{1}{2}$ *joules* of energy. In other words $4\frac{1}{2}$ J of energy would be produced as heat in the bulb for every coulomb of charge that passes through it. If the voltage across the bulb was 10 V, it means that the work done in moving 1 C of charge through the bulb would be 10 J.

From the above we can say that if *1 joule of work is done in moving 1 coulomb of charge between two points in a circuit, the voltage between the points is 1 volt.*

Thus the volt may be defined as

$$1 \text{ Volt } = 1 \text{ Joule per coulomb}$$

Therefore

$$\text{Energy or work done} = \text{Voltage} \times \text{Charge}$$

$$\text{or} \quad W = VQ \qquad [1.3]$$

POTENTIAL DIFFERENCE (PD) AND ELECTROMOTIVE FORCE (EMF)____

The voltage between any two points in a circuit is also known as the difference in electrical potential between these points. Therefore, potential difference (abbreviated to p.d.) is measured in volts, and this is what a voltmeter connected between the two points would indicate.

The potential difference or voltage that exists across a part of a circuit, say a resistor, can be represented in one of three ways, as shown in Fig. 1.8. In Fig. 1.8(a) symbols + and − are placed at the ends of the resistor and the V alongside. The + is placed at the end where the current enters the resistor. These signs give us a reference direction for the voltage, so that if we say $V = +8\,\text{V}$ it means the + end of the resistor is positive with respect to the − end. If $V = -3\,\text{V}$, it would mean that the end we have labelled + would actually, at that instant, be negative with respect to the other end. In Fig. 1.8(b) voltage or p.d. is represented by an arrow, the tip of the arrow indicating the positive end. A third method is to use double subscripts as in Fig. 1.8(c). If $V_{\text{AB}} = +3\,\text{V}$, this means that 'A is positive with respect to B' by 3 V.

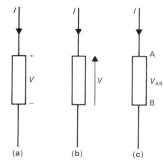

Fig. 1.8   Three ways of representing a voltage across a resistor

Potential difference may be thought of as a difference in 'electrical height'. In the same way as we measure the height of a mountain with reference to sea level, so the electrical potential of a point A is its electrical 'height' above some reference B as shown in Fig. 1.9(a). If the voltages or p.d.s between each of two points and a common reference are known, then the voltage between those two points can easily be calculated. For example, see Fig. 1.9(b).

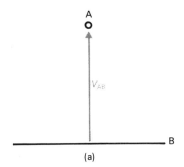

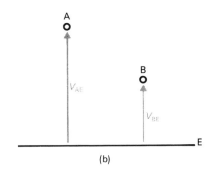

Fig. 1.9   Electrical potential as height

If we require V_{AB} but only know V_{AE} and V_{BE}, then

$$V_{AB} = V_{AE} - V_{BE}$$

So if $V_{AB} = +10\,V$ and $V_{BE} = +7\,V$, then the potential difference between A and B, V_{AB}, will be 3 V. The analogy with measuring height above a common reference point should be obvious.

We have seen that the voltage across a part of a circuit is related to the work done in joules for a coulomb of charge passing through it. The energy comes, of course, from the *electrical source* in the circuit, in our case the battery, as previously stated. The fact that a voltage exists across the battery terminals is an indication that it possesses energy. This voltage known as the battery *terminal voltage* may be slightly less than the voltage actually 'generated' within the battery, due to losses in the battery itself. The voltage existing within the battery is the real 'force' responsible for driving a current through a circuit, and is known as *electromotive force* (e.m.f.). It is, of course, also measured in volts.

Thus, a battery of e.m.f. 9 V would have to supply 9 J of energy to cause 1 C of charge to flow through a circuit. Some of the energy would be used internally in the battery (losses) the remainder being converted into heat or mechanical work in the 'external' circuit. To summarise:

The e.m.f. (V) is a measure of the energy generated per C by the source. The p.d. (V) is a measure of the energy dissipated per C by the external circuit.

Both e.m.f. and p.d. are measured in volts, and frequently it is better to refer to e.m.f. as *generated voltage*, i.e. the voltage produced by any source, be it a battery or electromechanical generator such as an alternator. Similarly p.d. is frequently referred to as *voltage drop* or simply as *voltage*.

WORKED EXAMPLE 3

An electric fire has 240 V across it and the current through it is 2 A. Calculate: (a) the charge passing through it in 1 h, (b) the energy output over 1 h.

SOLUTION

(a) Charge (C) = Current (A) × Time (s)   (equation [1.2])

$$= 2 \times 60 \times 60 = 7200 \, C$$

(b) Energy (J) = Voltage (V) × Charge (C)   (equation [1.3])

$$= 240 \times 7200$$

$$= 1.728 \times 10^6 \, J$$

WORKED EXAMPLE 4

Three points in an electrical circuit are labelled A, B and C. A voltmeter connected between A and C measures 10 V, between B and C 6 V. Calculate: (a) the voltmeter reading if connected between A and B, (b) the work done in transferring 2 C of charge between A and B.

SOLUTION

(a) $V_{AB} = V_{AC} - V_{BC}$

$$= 10 - 6 = 4 \, V$$

(b) Work done = Voltage × Charge transferred   (equation [1.3])

$$= 4 \, V \times 2 \, C = 8 \, J$$

WORKED EXAMPLE 5

A resistor is connected across a battery of e.m.f. 12 V. The voltage across the resistor is 11.8 V, and the current is constant for 200 s at 0.5 A. Calculate: (a) the heat energy produced in the resistor over 200 s, (b) the energy produced by the battery over 200 s and account for the difference between this and the answer of (a).

SOLUTION

(a) Work done = Voltage (V) × Charge (Q)   (equation [1.3])

$$= \text{Voltage } (V) \times \text{Current } (A) \times \text{Time (s)}$$

$$= 11.8 \times 0.5 \times 200$$

$$= 1180 \, J$$

(b) Energy = Voltage (V) × Charge (Q)   (equation [1.3])

$$= 12 \times 100$$

$$= 1200 \, J$$

This is 20 J greater than the heat energy produced in (a) the resistor. The difference is due to energy losses within the battery. These losses would appear as heat in the battery.

RESISTANCE

The value of resistance of any component (e.g. a bulb or resistor) is obtained by dividing the voltage across the component by the current that flows through the component. Thus for the bulb shown in the circuit of Fig. 1.1

$$\text{Bulb resistance } (R) = \frac{\text{Voltage across bulb (V)}}{\text{Current through bulb (A)}}$$

The unit of resistance is the *ohm* (symbol Ω). In the above equation it is essential that voltage is in *volts* and *current* in amperes.

Resistance is thus the ratio of voltage to current. For a given voltage the greater the resistance, the less will be the current. *Resistance is, therefore, a measure of the 'hindrance' provided by a component or circuit to the flow of current.*

The value of the resistance of a component need not be constant. For example, in the circuit of Fig. 1.1 the current through the bulb may be 150 mA when the voltage across it is 4.5 V, and 250 mA when the voltage is 9 V. The resistance in each case will be

Case 1   Resistance $R = \dfrac{4.5\,\text{V}}{150 \times 10^{-3}\,\text{A}} = \dfrac{4.5 \times 10^3}{150} = 30\,\Omega$

Case 2   Resistance $R = \dfrac{9\,\text{V}}{250 \times 10^{-3}\,\text{A}} = \dfrac{9 \times 10^3}{250} = 36\,\Omega$

The reason for this is that the temperature of the bulb will be different in each case (it will burn brighter in case 2 than in case 1), and as we shall see later, resistance varies with temperature.

Because the bulb resistance does not stay constant and varies with the current through it (or the voltage across it), the bulb is said to be a *non-linear* component. As can be seen from the above cases, doubling the voltage from 4.5 V to 9 V did not double the current. If we draw a graph of I against V, it will not be a straight line but a curve and therefore, termed a 'non-linear' characteristic, as shown in Fig. 1.10(a).

Resistors are components designed to have a constant value of resistance. A typical construction uses a length of nichrome wire (whose resistance does not vary much with temperature) wound on a former. Such resistors are used to limit and control current in electrical circuits. In such cases if the resistance is constant, then the current through the resistor will be proportional to the voltage across the resistor. That is, if the voltage is doubled the current is doubled, and a graph of I against V will be a straight line or linear, as shown in Fig. 1.10(b).

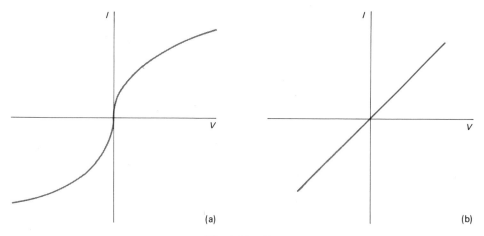

Fig. 1.10   Non-linear and linear resistor characteristics

OHM'S LAW

In the above case of constant resistance we have

$$\frac{V}{I} = R = \text{Constant, which is the value of } R$$

or
$$V = IR \quad \text{or} \quad I = \frac{V}{R}$$

That is, if R is constant, I is proportional to V. This is Ohm's law, which can be simply stated as

> Current is proportional to voltage

RELATIONSHIP BETWEEN CURRENT, VOLTAGE AND RESISTANCE

The resistance, R, of a component is defined by $R = V/I$. Rearranging gives

$$V = IR \quad \text{and} \quad I = \frac{V}{R}$$

These three equations are important. They relate V and I for a resistance whose value is R [Fig. 1.11(a)]. Fig. 1.11(a) can be regarded as a statement of Ohm's law. A sample aid for memory is shown in Fig. 1.11(b). To find R cover R with your finger and the answer is 'V upon I'. Similarly I is 'V upon R' and V is 'I times R'.

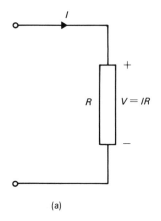

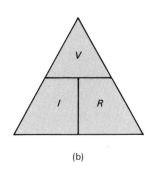

(a)   (b)

Fig. 1.11   Relationship between *V, I* and *R*

WORKED EXAMPLE 6

The current-voltage relationship for a non-linear resistor is given in Fig. 1.12(a). If this resistor is used in the circuit of Fig. 1.12(b), calculate: (a) the current through the resistor when the switch is (i) in position A, (ii) in position B; (b) the actual resistance value under both conditions.

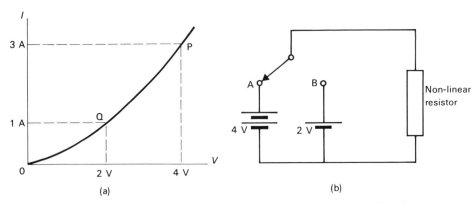

(a)   (b)

Fig. 1.12   Information for Worked Example 6

SOLUTION

(a)   (i)   When the switch is in position A the voltage across the resistor will be 4 V and the current will be given by the current corresponding to point P on the curve, i.e. 3 A.

(ii)   When the switch is at B, the voltage will be 2 V, corresponding to point Q on the graph, and the current will, therefore, be 1 A.

(b)   Since $R = \dfrac{V}{I}$ for (i) we have $R = \dfrac{4\,V}{3\,A} = 1.33\,\Omega$ and for (ii) $R = \dfrac{2\,V}{1\,A} = 2\,\Omega.$

These values confirm that R is not constant, i.e. the resistor is non-linear.

WORKED EXAMPLE 7

For the circuit shown in Fig. 1.13 R is a constant resistor of 2 Ω. The switch is connected to A at $t = 0$ and after 1s switched to B and after a further 1s back to A and so on. (a) Sketch a graph of the voltage across R versus time for a period of 5s. (b) Sketch a graph of the current through R against time for the same 5 s.

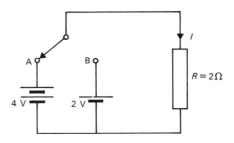

Fig. 1.13   Information for Worked Example 7

SOLUTION

(a)   The voltage across R will alternate between 4 V and 2 V every second as shown.

(b)   Using $I = \dfrac{V}{R}$, when the voltage is 4 V, $I = 4\,V/2\,\Omega = 2\,A$ and when $V = 2\,V$, $I = 2\,V/2\,\Omega = 1\,A.$

Therefore, the current waveform will be as shown.

It should be observed that the voltage and current waveforms are the same shape, and are 'in step' in time.

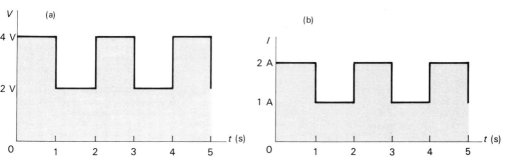

Fig. 1.14   Solution to Worked Example 7

ELECTRICAL POWER

We have already seen that the work-done in transferring a charge Q through a voltage V is given by

$$\text{Work done (J)} = \text{Volts} \times \text{Coulombs}$$

Now, since power is the work done per second, we can divide both sides of the equation by time to give

$$\text{Power} = \text{Work done/second} = \text{Volts} \times \text{Coulombs/second}$$

or   Power = Volts $\times$ Current

that is $P = VI$ [1.4]

The unit of power is joule per second or watt.

In Fig. 1.15 the power taken by resistor R which appears as heat will be given by

$$P = V \times I \text{ watts}$$

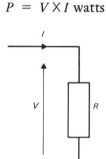

Fig. 1.15   Expression for power in R

Now for this circuit V is also given by $V = IR$, and substituting this in the first expression we have

$$P = IR \times I$$

or $P = I^2R$ [1.5]

This is an important expression for power and should be memorised.

WORKED EXAMPLE 8

A current of 2 A flows through a resistor of 100 Ω.

(a)   Calculate the power dissipated in the resistor under these conditions.

(b)   If the following changes are made one at a time, state which will produce the greatest change in heat output, and calculate the value in each case:

    (i)   the resistance is increased by 20%, the current remaining constant at 2 A;

    (ii)   the current is increased by 20% whilst the resistance remains constant.

SOLUTION

(a)   Since   Power $= I^2R$ (equation [1.5]) then for (a) $P = (2)^2 \times 100 = 400\,\text{W}$.

(b)   The power dissipated in the resistor which appears as heat will be proportional to the square of the current, and only directly proportional to the value of the resistance. Therefore, increasing the current will produce the greater change in heat output. This can be seen by calculating the power:

In case (i) $P = 2^2 \times 120 = 480\,\text{W}$.

In case (ii) $P = (2.4)^2 \times 100 = 576\,\text{W}$.

Thus, in case (i) the power increases by 80 W and in case (ii) by 176 W.

RESISTORS IN SERIES _____

Fig. 1.16 shows resistors connected in series — that is, the end of one resistor is connected to the start of the next. <u>The effective resistance of a number of resistors connected in series is equal to the sum of the individual resistors.</u>

Thus in Fig. 1.16, the effective resistance between A and B is

$$R = R_1 + R_2 + R_3 \qquad\qquad [1.6]$$

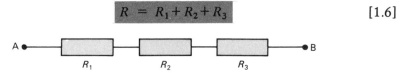

Fig. 1.16   Resistors in series

WORKED EXAMPLE 9

In Fig. 1.16, $R_1 = 500\,\Omega$, $R_2 = 125\,\Omega$ and $R_3 = 80\,\Omega$. What is the effective resistance between A and B?

SOLUTION

The resistors are connected in series and hence the effective resistance between A and B is, from equation [1.6],

$$R = R_1 + R_2 + R_3$$
$$= 500 + 125 + 80$$
$$= 705\,\Omega$$

RESISTORS IN PARALLEL _____

Fig. 1.17 shows resistors connected in parallel, that is, the resistors are connected across each other. The value of the effective resistance R is found by using

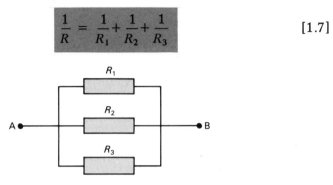

$$\frac{1}{R} = \frac{1}{R_1} + \frac{1}{R_2} + \frac{1}{R_3} \qquad [1.7]$$

Fig. 1.17   Resistors in parallel

WORKED EXAMPLE 10

In Fig. 1.17, $R_1 = 20\,\Omega$, $R_2 = 30\,\Omega$ and $R_3 = 60\,\Omega$. Find the effective resistance of the circuit.

SOLUTION

The resistors are connected in parallel and hence the effective resistance of the circuit is obtained from equation [1.7]:

$$\frac{1}{R} = \frac{1}{R_1} + \frac{1}{R_2} + \frac{1}{R_3}$$

$$\frac{1}{R} = \frac{1}{20} + \frac{1}{30} + \frac{1}{60} = \frac{1}{10}$$

$$R = 10\,\Omega$$

SOME USEFUL POINTS ABOUT RESISTORS IN PARALLEL _____

(a) For two resistors in parallel the equation $\dfrac{1}{R} = \dfrac{1}{R_1} + \dfrac{1}{R_2}$ becomes

$$R = \frac{R_1 R_2}{R_1 + R_2}$$

Memorise this equation and always use it for two resistors in parallel.

(b) If a number of identical resistors are connected in parallel their effective resistance will be the value of one of them divided by the number of resistors in parallel. For example, three resistors of $100\,\Omega$ in parallel will have an effective value of $100/3 = 33.3\,\Omega$.

(c) The effective value of any number of resistors connected in parallel will be less than the value of the least of them.

VOLTAGES IN A SERIES CIRCUIT

Fig. 1.18(a) shows a circuit with R_1 and R_2 in series. A current will flow through the circuit, and consequently voltages V_{CD} and V_{EF} will appear across R_1 and R_2 respectively. The voltages can be represented as in Fig. 1.18(b).

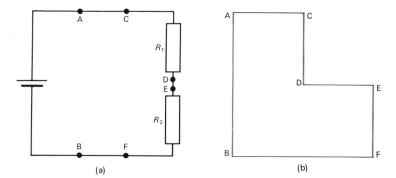

Fig. 1.18 Voltages in a series circuit

The battery voltage is represented by AB. Points A and C are at the same 'level' as they are connected by a wire which has zero resistance. CD is the voltage across R_1 and again since D and E are connected by a wire they are at the same 'level' as are points B and F.

From Fig. 1.18(b) we see that the 'height' of C above F is CD + EF or, translated into voltages,

$$V_{CF} = V_{CD} + V_{EF}$$

Furthermore the difference in 'height' between A and B is the same as that between C and F, so we have

$$V_{AB} = V_{CF} = V_{CD} + V_{EF}$$

or simply $V_{AB} = V_{CD} + V_{EF}$.

This can be stated as a general principle:

> In a series circuit the sum of the voltages across the resistors
> in the circuit is equal to the applied (battery) voltage.

WORKED EXAMPLE 11

A 110 V d.c. motor armature is to be operated from a 240 V d.c. supply. If under working conditions the motor takes a current of 0.65 A, calculate the value of resistor that should be connected in series with it.

SOLUTION

The circuit is shown below in Fig. 1.19. Since the motor and resistor are in series,

Supply voltage = Voltage across motor + Voltage across R

So the voltage across R will be $240 - 110 = 130$ V.

Now this voltage is given by $V_R = IR$, and since the current I is 0.65 A,

$$R = \frac{130}{0.65} = 200\,\Omega$$

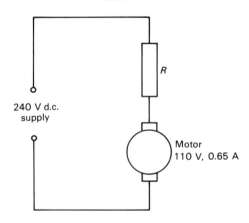

Fig. 1.19   Circuit for Worked Example 11

VOLTAGE DIVISION RULE _____

For two resistors R_1 and R_2 connected in series (Fig. 1.20) the voltage across R_2 is given by

$$V_2 = \frac{R_2}{R_1 + R_2}V$$

[1.8]

i.e. a fraction $\dfrac{R_2}{R_1 + R_2}$ of the applied voltage V appears across R_2.

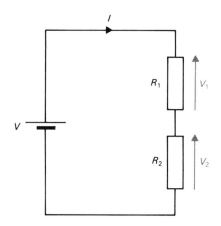

Fig. 1.20   Division of voltage between two resistors

This can be seen by noting that $V = IR$, where R is the effective resistance of R_1 and R_2 in series,

or $$V = I(R_1 + R_2) \qquad [1.9]$$

Also $$V_2 = IR_2 \qquad [1.10]$$

So dividing equation [1.10] by [1.9], we have

$$\frac{V_2}{V} = \frac{IR_2}{I(R_1 + R_2)}$$

or $$V_2 = \frac{R_2}{R_1 + R_2} V$$

This is an important and useful equation and should be memorised.

Also since $V_1 = IR_1$ and $V_2 = IR_2$, then

$$\frac{V_1}{V_2} = \frac{R_1}{R_2} \qquad [1.11]$$

Hence the voltage V divides between the resistor R_1 and R_2 in proportion to their ratio.

WORKED EXAMPLE 12

Calculate the voltage V_{BC} for the circuit shown in Fig. 1.21.

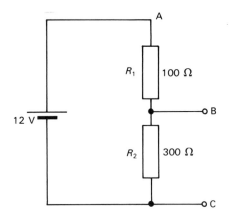

Fig. 1.21   Information for Worked Example 12

SOLUTION

We use equation [1.8]:

$$V_{BC} = \frac{R_2}{R_1 + R_2} \times 12\,V$$

$$= \frac{300}{300 + 100} \times 12\,V$$

$$= \tfrac{3}{4} \times 12\,V = 9\,V$$

WORKED EXAMPLE 13

A potential divider has its sliding contact set one quarter of the 'distance' from the bottom as shown in Fig. 1.22. Assuming the resistor is linear along its length calculate: (a) the voltage V_{BC} if $V_{AC} = 40\,V$, (b) the position the slider should be moved to in order that V_{BC} is 32 V.

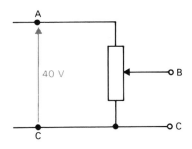

Fig. 1.22   Information for Worked Example 13

SOLUTION

(a) From equation [1.11],

$$V_{BC} = \frac{R_{BC}}{R_{AC}} \times V_{AC}$$

Since the resistance is proportional to length, R_{BC}/R_{AC} will be $\frac{1}{4}$ so

$$V_{BC} = \frac{1}{4} \times 40\,V = 10\,V$$

(b) To get a voltage of 32 V across V_{BC} means that point B must be 32/40th of the total 'distance' from the bottom. This can be proved from the equation in (a) for

$$\frac{V_{BC}}{V_{AC}} = \frac{R_{BC}}{R_{AC}} = \frac{L_{BC}}{L_{AC}} \quad \text{when } L \text{ represents 'length'}$$

so

$$\frac{L_{BC}}{L_{AC}} = \frac{32}{40} = \frac{8}{10}$$

CURRENTS IN A PARALLEL CIRCUIT _____

In Fig. 1.23(a), because the two resistors are connected in parallel, the current I will divide between them, I_1 going through R_1 and I_2 going through R_2. Since these currents have no other path to follow and the electrons do not accumulate anywhere, then

$$I = I_1 + I_2$$

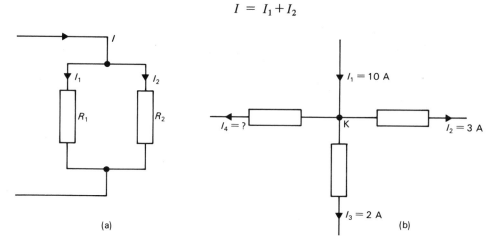

(a)

(b)

Fig. 1.23   Currents flowing towards a junction equal currents flowing away from the junction

Hence at any electrical junction — a point where three or more wires meet — the current flowing towards the junction equals the current flowing away from the junction.

As an example consider Fig. 1.23(b). If at the junction K the current flowing towards K is 10 A, the current flowing away from K is I_2, I_3 and I_4. Therefore

$$I_2 + I_3 + I_4 = 10\,\text{A}$$

So if $I_2 = 3$ A and $I_3 = 2$ A, then

$$3 + 2 + I_4 = 10$$

$$I_4 = 5\,\text{A}$$

WORKED EXAMPLE 14

A transistor has three terminals, labelled collector (C), emitter (E) and base (B), and its symbol is shown in Fig. 1.24. Three milliammeters are connected as indicated to measure the currents in the three leads. All meters read upscale and mA_1 reads 10.0 mA, mA_2 reads 10.3 mA.

(a)   State for each lead whether the current flows towards or away from the transistor.

(b)   Determine the reading of mA_3.

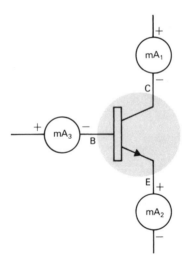

Fig. 1.24   Information for Worked Example 14

SOLUTION

(a)   Remembering that if the meters are to read upscale the current enters their (+) terminals, we have:

   (i)   current flows towards B and C,

   (ii)   current flows away from E.

(b) We can treat the transistor as a 'junction', so that

Current flowing towards transistor = Current flowing away from it

or $\qquad\qquad I_B + I_C = I_E$

so $\qquad\qquad\quad I_B = I_E - I_C$

$\qquad\qquad\qquad\quad = 10.3 - 10.0 = 0.3\,\text{mA}$

CURRENT DIVISION RULE

For two resistors connected in parallel (Fig. 1.25) the current I_1 in terms of the total current I is given by

$$I_1 = \frac{R_2}{R_1 + R_2} I \qquad\qquad [1.12]$$

that is, I_1 is a fraction $\dfrac{R_2}{R_1 + R_2}$ of I.

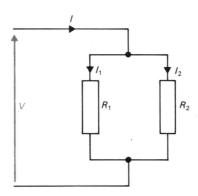

Fig. 1.25   Division of current between two resistors

This can be seen by noting that

$$I_1 = \frac{V}{R_1}$$

and $\qquad\qquad I = \dfrac{V}{R_\text{eq}} \quad \text{where} \quad R_\text{eq} = \dfrac{R_1 R_2}{R_1 + R_2}$

So dividing: $\qquad \dfrac{I_1}{I} = \dfrac{V}{R_1} \cdot \dfrac{R_\text{eq}}{V} = \dfrac{I}{R_1} \cdot \dfrac{R_1 R_2}{R_1 + R_2}$

or $\qquad\qquad\qquad I_1 = \dfrac{R_2}{R_1 + R_2} I$

It is also useful to note that since

$$I_1 = V/R_1 \quad \text{and} \quad I_2 = V/R_2$$

$$\frac{I_1}{I_2} = \frac{R_2}{R_1} \qquad [1.13]$$

and so the current divides between the resistor R_1 and R_2 in the *inverse ratio* of their resistances. This is, of course, only another way of saying that the greater current will flow through the resistor having the least resistance.

Both voltage and current division rules have the same form, but note the difference in the numerator. In each case

For resistors in series

$$\text{Voltage across } R_2 = \frac{\text{Value of } R_2}{R_1 + R_2} \text{ of total voltage}$$

For resistors in parallel

$$\text{Current through } R_2 = \frac{\text{Value of } R_1}{R_1 + R_2} \text{ of total current}$$

WORKED EXAMPLE 15

For the circuit shown in Fig. 1.26 calculate the current through each resistor if the total current is $I = 220\,\text{mA}$.

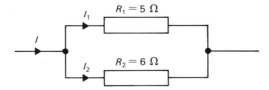

Fig. 1.26   Information for Worked Example 15

SOLUTION

Using equation [1.12], $I_1 = \dfrac{R_2}{R_1 + R_2} I$

$$I_1 = \frac{6}{5 + 6} \times 220\,\text{mA}$$

$$= \frac{6}{11} \times 220\,\text{mA} = 120\,\text{mA}$$

To find I_2 we could use

$$I_2 = I - I_1 = 220 - 120 = 100 \, \text{mA}$$

or alternatively

$$I_2 = \frac{R_1}{R_1 + R_2} \times 220 \, \text{mA}$$

$$= \frac{5}{11} \times 220 \, \text{mA} = 100 \, \text{mA}$$

CIRCUIT CALCULATIONS

The electrical circuits we shall consider here are made up of a single voltage source (e.g. battery) and several resistors. The resistors may be connected in series, in parallel, or in a mixture of both. The problems usually are of the following types:

(a)   Given a circuit with the values of the source voltage and resistors, calculate the voltages and currents in any part of the circuit.

(b)   Given a circuit calculate the required value of resistors, so that the current or voltage may be as specified in any part of the circuit. In some cases you may be asked to design a circuit for a particular purpose.

The rules and laws we have already discussed will enable us to undertake this analysis and design of circuits. We make use of the following:

(a)   Voltage, current and resistance of any component are related by the equation $V = IR$, so if we know any two of these quantities, the third can be calculated.

(b)   In a series circuit, or in a closed loop of any circuit, the voltages across each component add up to the applied voltage. This is sometimes referred to as *Kirchhoff's voltage law.*

(c)   At any junction in a circuit, the sum of the currents flowing towards the junction equals the sum of the currents flowing away from the junction. This is sometimes referred to as *Kirchhoff's current law.*

(d)   Two or more resistors in series may be replaced by a single resistor whose value is given by $R = R_1 + R_2 + \ldots$ (equation [1.6]).

(e)   Two or more resistors in parallel may be replaced by a single resistor whose value is given by

$$R = \frac{R_1 R_2}{R_1 + R_2} \quad \text{or} \quad \frac{1}{R} = \frac{1}{R_1} + \frac{1}{R_1} + \ldots \quad \text{(equation [1.7])}$$

(f)   For two resistors in series the voltages divide between them such that

$$V_2 = \frac{R_2}{R_1 + R_2} \text{ of total voltage across both of them} \quad \text{(equation [1.8])}$$

(g)   For two resistors in parallel the current divides between them such that

$$I_2 = \frac{R_1}{R_1 + R_2} \text{ of the total current} \quad \text{(equation [1.12])}$$

WORKED EXAMPLE 16

In Fig. 1.27(a), $R_1 = 6\,\Omega$, $R_2 = 12\,\Omega$ and $R_3 = 5\,\Omega$. Calculate the current flowing in each resistor.

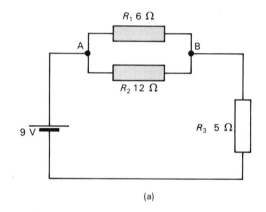

(a)

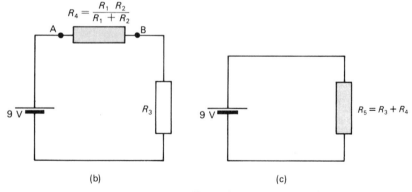

(b)   (c)

Fig. 1.27   Information for Worked Example 16

SOLUTION

Step 1. R_1 and R_2 are connected in parallel and can therefore be replaced by a single resistor which we will call R_4 as shown in Fig. 1.27(b). Its value will be

$$R_4 = \frac{R_1 R_2}{R_1 + R_2} = \frac{6 \times 12}{6 + 12} = 4\,\Omega$$

Step 2. R_4 and R_3 are connected in series and can therefore be replaced by a single resistor which we will call R_5 as shown in Fig. 1.27(c) such that

$$R_5 = R_3 + R_4 = 5 + 4 = 9\,\Omega$$

Step 3. The voltage across R_5 is 9 V. Hence the current through R_5 will be given by

$$I = \frac{V}{R_5} = \frac{9\,V}{9\,\Omega} = 1\,A$$

This will be the current supplied by the battery, and it flows through our resistor R_4 and the resistor R_3.

Step 4. The easiest way to find the current through R_1 and R_2 is to first find the voltage across them. This voltage will be that across R_4 which is

$$V_{AB} = IR_4 = 1 \times 4 = 4\,V$$

Hence the current through R_1 will be $\dfrac{4\,V}{6\,\Omega} = \dfrac{2}{3}\,A$

and the current through R_2 will be $\dfrac{4\,V}{12\,\Omega} = \dfrac{1}{3}\,A.$

Check. You should always check that your answers make sense. In this case we note that at junction A we have 1 A flowing towards the junction and $(\frac{2}{3} + \frac{1}{3})$ flowing away which correctly adds up to 1 A.

We also note that the voltage across R_3 is 5 V, and that across R_4 is 4 V, adding up to 9 V which is the battery voltage. We could have used this fact to calculate the voltage V_{AB} by saying that

$$\text{Battery voltage} = V_{AB} + \text{Voltage across } R_3$$
$$V_{AB} = \text{Battery voltage} - \text{Voltage across } R_3$$
$$V_{AB} = 9 - (5 \times 1) = 4\,V$$

WORKED EXAMPLE 17

It is desired to connect two bulbs in series to a 12 V battery. The bulbs are rated at 6 V, 0.5 A and 4.5 V, 0.4 A. Design a suitable circuit using any additional resistors that may be required.

SOLUTION

A possible circuit is shown in Fig. 1.28. There are two problems here:

(a) The bulb voltages add up to only 10.5 V, so we have to include a series resistor R_1 so that 1.5 V will appear across it.

(b) The bulbs are of different current rating, and since 0.5 A must flow through bulb 1 and only 0.4 A through bulb 2, we shunt 0.1 A through R_2 as shown in the diagram.

Our problem, therefore, is to find the values of R_1 and R_2.

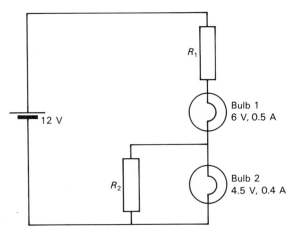

Fig. 1.28   Information for Worked Example 17

Step 1. The current through the circuit should be that through bulb 1. That is, it should be 4.5 V, and 0.5 A which will also be the current through R_1. Since 1.5 V must exist across R_1, the value of R_1 will be

$$R_1 = \frac{1.5\,V}{0.5\,A} = 3\,\Omega$$

Step 2. We note that the voltage across R_2 will be the same as that across bulb 2, that is since the current through R_2 is 0.1 A, we have

$$R_2 = \frac{4.5\,V}{0.1\,A} = 45\,\Omega$$

WORKED EXAMPLE 18

For the circuit of Fig. 1.29(a): (a) Calculate the effective resistance between A and B. (b) What will be the value of currents I_1, I_2 and I_3, if 50 V is applied between A and B?

SOLUTION

(a)   The problem here is to replace all the resistors between A and B by a single resistor. This can be done in three steps as shown.

   Step 1. The two 150 Ω resistors that are in series are combined to give one resistor of 300 Ω.

   Step 2. The 150 Ω and 300 Ω resistors which are now in parallel are combined to give one resistor.

   We use $$R = \frac{R_1 R_2}{R_1 + R_2} = \frac{150 \times 300}{450} = 100\,\Omega$$

   Note that a quick way to do this is to say that the 150 Ω could be made up from *two* 300 Ω resistors in parallel. We then would have *three* 300 Ω in parallel so that the equivalent resistance is 300/3 or 100 Ω.

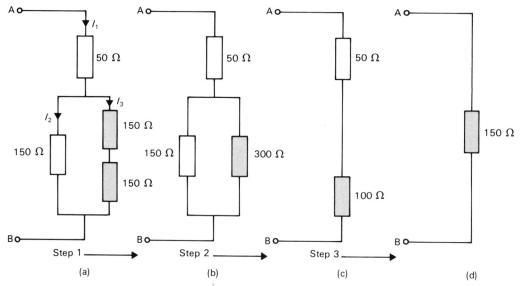

Fig. 1.29 Information for Worked Example 18 and steps for solution

Step 3. The 100 Ω and 50 Ω resistors are now in series and give an effective resistance of 150 Ω between A and B.

(b) I_1 is the total current that will flow in the circuit and is given by

$$I_1 = \frac{50\,\text{V}}{150\,\Omega} = 0.33\,\text{A}$$

This current will divide, part of it I_2 flowing through the 150 Ω resistor, and the other I_3 flowing through what is effectively 300 Ω. Since these two paths are in parallel and one path is one-half the resistance of the other the current will divide in the ratio 2 : 1. Therefore, I_2 will be 0.22 A and I_3 will be 0.11 A.

WORKED EXAMPLE 19

For the circuit shown in Fig. 1.30, without calculating the current, determine the voltage between C and D.

SOLUTION

For R_1 and R_2 we note that the battery voltage of 12 V exists across them. Using the voltage division rule we then have that

$$V_{\text{CB}} = \frac{R_2}{R_1 + R_2} V_{\text{AB}}$$

$$= \frac{20}{10 + 20} \times 12 = 8\,\text{V}$$

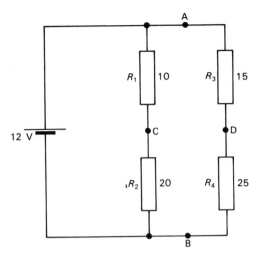

Fig. 1.30   Information for Worked Example 19

Similarly

$$V_{DB} = \frac{R_4}{R_3 + R_4} V_{AB} = \frac{25}{15 + 25} \times 12 = 7.5\,V$$

Now

$$V_{CD} = V_{CB} - V_{DB} = (8 - 7.5)\,V = 0.5\,V$$

WORKED EXAMPLE 20

For the circuit shown in Fig. 1.31 calculate: (a) the current through each of the resistors, (b) the voltage between C and D.

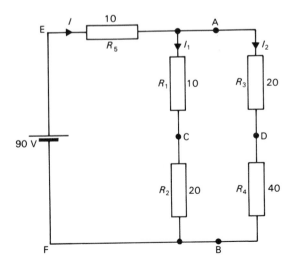

Fig. 1.31   Information for Worked Example 20

SOLUTION

(a)   (i)   We note that R_1 and R_2 can be replaced by a single resistor

$$R_a = R_1 + R_2 = 30\,\Omega$$

Similarly for R_3 and R_4

$$R_b = R_3 + R_4 = 60\,\Omega$$

(ii)   Then R_a and R_b are in parallel so the effective resistance between A and B is

$$R_{AB} = \frac{R_a R_b}{R_a + R_b} = \frac{30 \times 60}{30 + 60} = 20\,\Omega$$

(iii) R_{AB} will be in series with R_5, so $R_{EF} = R_5 + R_{AB}$

$$R_{EF} = 10 + 20 = 30\,\Omega$$

(iv)   Therefore the current supplied by the battery $I = \dfrac{90\,V}{30\,\Omega} = 3\,A$

(b)   There are two ways of proceeding from here to find V_{CD}.

Method 1. Since the $R_1 R_2$ path is $30\,\Omega$ and the $R_3 R_4$ path is $60\,\Omega$ it is easy to deduce that twice the current that goes through the $60\,\Omega$ will go through the $30\,\Omega$. The current will, therefore, divide in the ratio 2:1, i.e. 2 A flows through R_1 and R_2 and 1 A through R_3 and R_4.

Alternatively we can use the current division rule to find I_1:

$$I_1 = \frac{60}{60 + 30} I = \frac{2}{3} \times 3\,A = 2\,A$$

and

$$I_2 = I - I_1 = (3 - 2)\,A = 1\,A$$

Now

$$V_{CD} = V_{CB} - V_{DB}$$
$$V_{CB} = I_1 R_2 = 2 \times 20 = 40\,V$$
$$V_{DB} = I_3 R_4 = 1 \times 40 = 40\,V$$

and therefore

$$V_{CD} = 40 - 40 = 0$$

In other words points C and D are at the same electrical 'height' above point B.

Method 2. We note that since $I = 3\,A$, the voltage drop across R_5 will be

$$I R_5 = 3 \times 10 = 30\,V$$

Hence $V_{AB} = 90\,V - 30\,V = 60\,V$.

Using the voltage division rule gives

$$V_{CB} = \frac{R_2}{R_1 + R_2} V_{AB} = \frac{20}{30} V_{AB} = \frac{2}{3} \times 60 = 40\,V$$

$$V_{DB} = \frac{R_4}{R_3 + R_4} V_{AB} = \frac{40}{60} V_{AB} = \frac{2}{3} \times 60 = 40\,V$$

INTERNAL RESISTANCE

Earlier in this chapter we discussed that the e.m.f. of a battery or a cell was related to the energy to drive current around a circuit. Not all this energy is available for the 'outside' circuit, some of it being used up in the cell itself as losses. This is because during the production of current by a cell, energy is needed to move the charge through the chemicals inside the cell. Since the only component that can represent energy losses in an electrical circuit is a resistor, we talk of the cell having an *internal resistance r*. We use the standard symbol ○──┤├──○ for a cell or source without any internal losses, that is, the symbol represents an ideal cell.

To represent a 'real' battery we show an ideal cell in series with a resistor as shown in Fig. 1.32. If the losses are small, as they usually are, the resistor will have a low value. It must be emphasised that:

(a)   the only accessible parts of the cell are its two terminals, i.e. you cannot get at the junction between the 'resistor' and the ideal cell;

(b)   no actual resistor exists inside the cell, the cell characteristics are such as if this was the case.

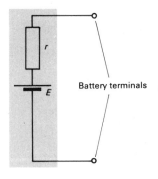

Battery terminals

Fig. 1.32   Circuit representing an actual cell

The voltage of the ideal cell is called its electromotive force (e.m.f.) and is usually given the symbol E.

The voltage across the terminal of the cell when no current is taken from it will be E volts — since if no current flows through r, there is no voltage drop across it. When any current is taken from the cell *the terminal voltage V will be less than E.*

It is quite easy to take the effect of internal resistance into account in circuit calculations as follows. Fig. 1.33 shows a cell connected to an external resistor R (often called the 'load'). A current I flows in the circuit. We have

$$E = \text{Voltage across } R + \text{Voltage across } r$$

or $\qquad E = IR + Ir$ $\hfill$ [1.14]

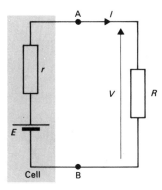

Fig. 1.33   A cell connected to an external resistor R, showing the effect of internal resistance r

This can be interpreted as IR volts being needed to drive the current through the external resistance and Ir volts to drive the current through the internal resistance of the cell. Since IR is the same thing as the terminal voltage V, then:

$$E = V + Ir$$

or $\qquad V = E - Ir$

The quantity Ir is sometimes called *lost volts.*

Thus the terminal voltage of a cell, when a current is drawn from it, is always less than the e.m.f. of the cell. The less the current, the smaller will be the 'volts lost' in the internal resistance of the cell. If the current is zero, no volts will be lost and the terminal voltage of the cell will be its e.m.f. E. In this condition, it means that no current is taken from the cell. In other words we have an open circuit. Therefore we can define e.m.f. as

e.m.f. = Terminal voltage of cell on open circuit

WORKED EXAMPLE 21

Fig. 1.34 shows a battery of e.m.f. 3.0 V and internal resistance 0.5 Ω connected to a resistor R. Calculate the terminal voltage of the cell if R has the following values (in Ω): 80, 15, 8, 2, 1 and 0.5.

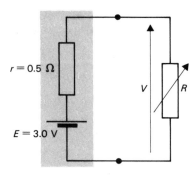

Fig. 1.34   Circuit for Worked Example 21

SOLUTION

First find the current in the circuit for each value of R. This will be given by $3.0\,V \div$ (effective resistance). The terminal voltage is then found by multiplying the current by R (see the table below).

$R(\Omega)$	80	15	8	2	1	0.5
$I = \dfrac{E}{R+r}$	$\dfrac{3}{80.5}$	$\dfrac{3}{15.5}$	$\dfrac{3}{8.5}$	$\dfrac{3}{2.5}$	$\dfrac{3}{1.5}$	$\dfrac{3}{1.0}$
$V = IR$	$\dfrac{3}{80.5} \times 80$ $= 2.98$	$\dfrac{3}{15.5} \times 15$ $= 2.90$	$\dfrac{3}{8.5} \times 8$ $= 2.82$	$\dfrac{3}{2.5} \times 2$ $= 2.40$	$\dfrac{3}{1.5} \times 1$ $= 2.00$	$\dfrac{3}{1.0} \times 0.5$ $= 1.50$

EXERCISE 1 _____

Multi-choice questions

1)   If an electric charge of 50 C flows past a point in 10 s, the average current is:

   a 500 mA   b 5 A   c 0.2 A   d 500 A

2)   Three wires meet a point P. Wire 1 carries a current of 5 A towards P; wire 2 carries a current of 3 A away from P. The charge that flows towards P in the third wire in 2 s will be:

   a 16 C   b 4 C   c −16 C   d −4 C

3)   The volt is the same as:

   a ampere per ohm   b watt per second
   c joule per coulomb   d coulomb per metre

4) The work done if a charge of 5 C is moved through a potential difference of 10 V is:

   a 50 J   b 2 J   c 0.5 J   d 10 J

5) The effective resistance between A and B in Fig. 1.35 is:

   a 50 Ω   b 20 Ω   c 35 Ω   d 15 Ω

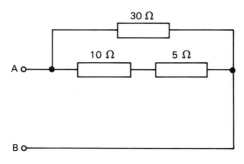

Fig. 1.35

6) The effective resistance between A and B in Fig. 1.36 is:

   a 45 Ω   b 15 Ω   c 0 Ω   d 10 Ω

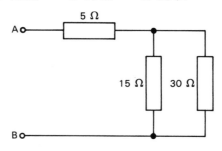

Fig. 1.36

7) The effective resistance between A and B in Fig. 1.37 will, when the switch S is closed:

   a become zero   b not change
   c increase   d decrease

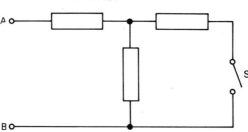

Fig. 1.37

8) The effective resistance between A and B in Fig. 1.38 will, when the switch S is closed:

a become zero   b not change
c increase   d become infinite

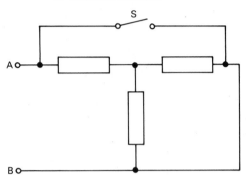

Fig. 1.38

9) The effective resistance between A and B in Fig. 1.39 will be *approximately*:

a 1Ω   b 20Ω   c 40Ω   d 10Ω

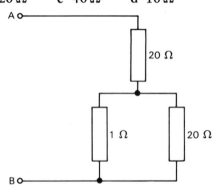

Fig. 1.39

10) The effective resistance between A and B in Fig. 1.40 will be given by:

a $\dfrac{1}{R} = \dfrac{1}{R_1} + \dfrac{1}{R_2} + \dfrac{1}{R_3}$ b $R = \dfrac{R_3(R_1 + R_2)}{R_1 + R_2 + R_3}$

c $R = R_1 + R_2 + R_3$ d $R = \dfrac{R_1 + R_2}{R_3}$

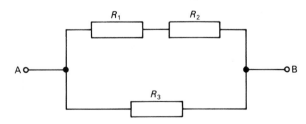

Fig. 1.40

11)   The effective resistance between A and B in Fig. 1.41 will be:

a $R_1 + 3R_2 + R_1$ **b** $\dfrac{R_1}{2} + \dfrac{R_2}{3}$

c $2R_1 + \dfrac{R_2}{3}$ **d** $2\left(R_1 + \dfrac{R_2}{3}\right)$

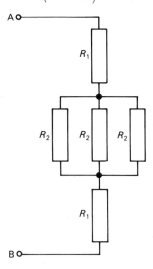

Fig. 1.41

12)   The voltage V_3 across R_3 in Fig. 1.42 will be given by:

a $V_3 = \dfrac{R_1 + R_2}{R_1 + R_2 + R_3} V_{AB}$ **b** $V_3 = \dfrac{R_1 + R_2}{R_3} V_{AB}$

c $V_3 = \dfrac{R_3}{R_1 + R_2} V_{AB}$ **d** $V_3 = \dfrac{R_3}{R_1 + R_2 + R_3} V_{AB}$

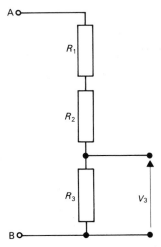

Fig. 1.42

13) The voltage *V* in Fig. 1.43 will be:

   a 10 V   b 5 V   c 15 V   d 20 V

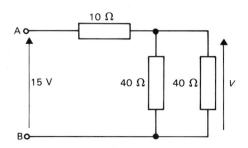

Fig. 1.43

14) The current *I* in Fig. 1.44 will be:

   a 10 A   b 5 A   c 15 A   d 3 A

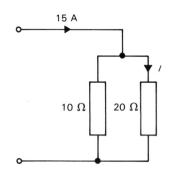

Fig. 1.44

15) The current *I* in Fig. 1.45 will be approximately:

   a 100 A   b 10 A   c 1 A   d 0.1 A

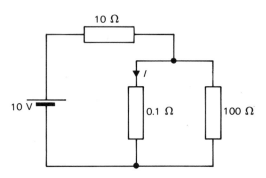

Fig. 1.45

Problems

16) In Fig. 1.46 calculate the value of R so that the bulb will operate at its correct rating.

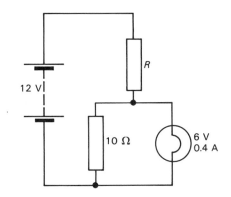

Fig. 1.46

17) In Fig. 1.47 calculate the value of R so that the bulb will operate at its correct rating.

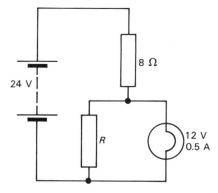

Fig. 1.47

18) In Fig. 1.48 calculate the value of V so that 1 A flows in the 2 Ω resistor.

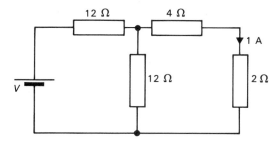

Fig. 1.48

19) In Fig. 1.49 calculate the values of the supply voltage V and the current I if the current taken from the supply is 5 A.

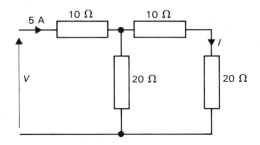

Fig. 1.49

20) Determine the position of the slider P along the linear resistor shown in Fig. 1.50 if the voltmeter V is to read zero. Would it make any difference if: (a) the 9 V battery was reversed? (b) both batteries were reversed?

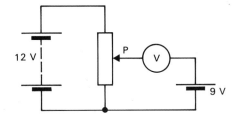

Fig. 1.50

21) In Fig. 1.51 calculate the value of R so that the voltmeter reads zero.

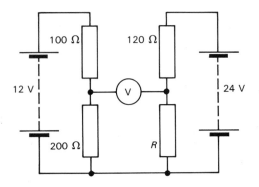

Fig. 1.51

22) A battery of e.m.f. 12 V and internal resistance $1\,\Omega$ is connected to a resistor of $10\,\Omega$. Calculate: (a) the current in the circuit, (b) the terminal voltage of the battery.

23) Two batteries, one e.m.f. 9 V and internal resistance 0.3 Ω and the other of e.m.f. 12 V and internal resistance 0.4 Ω, are connected in series as shown in Fig. 1.52 and a resistor of 5 Ω connected across them. Calculate: (a) the terminal voltage of each battery, (b) the voltage that would appear across A and B if the 5 Ω resistor were removed, (c) the current in the circuit if a short circuit were placed between A and B.

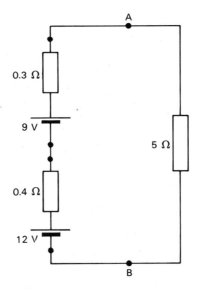

Fig. 1.52

THE MEASUREMENT
OF ELECTRICAL
QUANTITIES

After reaching the end of this chapter you should be able to:

1. *Sketch and label the movement of a moving-coil instrument.*
2. *Explain the action of a moving-coil instrument.*
3. *Explain the terms sensitivity, range, display, and accuracy in relation to electrical meters.*
4. *Describe the use of shunts and multimeters to extend the range of a basic meter movement and calculate their values.*
5. *Use voltmeters, ammeters and multipliers for measurements in d.c. circuits.*
6. *Describe the principles of operation of an ohmmeter.*
7. *Explain the use of potential dividers to give a simple variable d.c. supply.*

CONSTRUCTION AND OPERATION OF THE MOVING-COIL METER

The construction of a moving-coil meter is shown in Fig. 2.1(a) and Fig. 2.1(b). A coil of a few turns of enamelled wire is wound on an aluminium former which is suspended or pivoted in a magnetic field. The magnetic field in the air gap is provided by a permanent magnet.

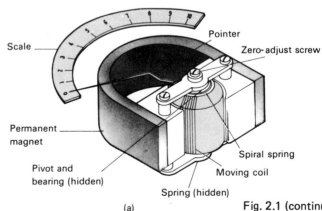

Scale

Pointer

Zero-adjust screw

Permanent magnet

Pivot and bearing (hidden)

Spring (hidden)

Spiral spring

Moving coil

(a)

Fig. 2.1 (continued opposite)

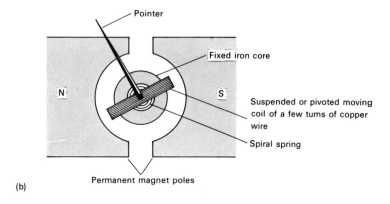

(b)

Fig. 2.1   Views of moving-coil meter. (b) is a plan view of (a)

The magnetic arrangement can take one of several forms, another arrangement is shown in Fig. 2.2. Current is fed into the two ends of the coil via the hair springs.

When a current is passed through the coil the following will happen:

(a)   A force or torque will act on the coil causing it to turn through a certain angle.

(b)   As the coil turns an opposing torque is provided by the hair springs.

The coil and pointer attached to it will come to rest at a point where these two torques are equal.

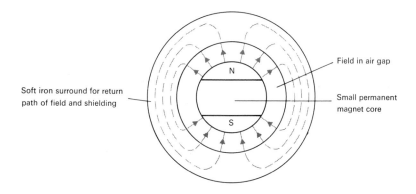

Fig. 2.2   Magnetic field system for a moving-coil meter

The torque in (a) produced by the coil will be proportional to the current. The opposing torque in (b) will be proportional to the angle through which the coil has turned. Hence we have

> **Angular deflection is proportional to current.**

This means that the meter scale will be linear as shown in Fig. 2.3(a) as compared with a non-linear scale [Fig. 2.3(b)] which exists with some other types of meters.

The angle through which the coil can turn is limited by stops so that the coil always lies in a uniform magnetic field. Usually the angle is of the order of 90°. A different arrangement of coil and magnet is used in *circular scale* meters which can have an angle of rotation of over 200° and consequently a longer scale length.

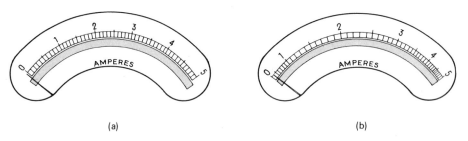

(a)   (b)

Fig. 2.3   Types of meter scale: (a) linear, (b) non-linear

THE NATURE OF MEASUREMENTS

The electrical quantities that are of chief interest are *voltage*, *current* and *resistance*. Electrical instruments or meters are available that can measure these directly, although it will be appreciated that if any two are measured the third can be calculated from Ohm's law. To measure the above quantities the engineer or technician has to:

(a) *select* an appropriate measuring instrument, that is, one which is of the correct *type*, the desired *range* and gives the necessary degree of accuracy;

(b) *use* it correctly for the measurement required, for example, attach it to the correct part of the circuit, use it safely and in the right position (e.g. some meters are calibrated for the horizontal position only);

(c) *interpret* the result of the measurement bearing in mind such things as errors and the effect or interference the instrument has on the circuit or system.

Some of the reasons for making measurements on systems are:

(a) for design purposes, when it may be necessary to find the voltage/current characteristic and behaviour of some component or device, e.g. the characteristic of a rolling mill motor in a steel works;

(b) for monitoring some quantities or the performance of a system, e.g. the current in an electroplating plant;

(c) for fault-finding in a circuit or system that is malfunctioning.

It should be noted that, although we may frequently measure the voltage 'output' of a system, the real thing we are interested in may be the speed or torque of a motor. Often the easiest way of measuring such quantities is by means of a *transducer*. This is a device that converts the 'mechanical' quantity into an electrical signal, frequently voltage. For this reason alone it is essential for mechanical engineers to be familiar with electrical circuits and measurements. Some quantities that may be 'transduced' are shown in Fig. 2.4.

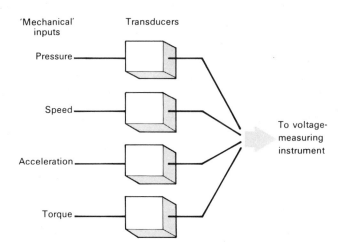

Fig. 2.4   Transducers

CHARACTERISTICS OF METERS _____

The important characteristics are *sensitivity, range, display* and *accuracy.*

SENSITIVITY _____

For a moving-coil meter sensitivity can be defined as the current required to produce *full-scale deflection* (abbreviated to f.s.d.). Since the moving coil is a *current-operated device*, at a certain value of current the pointer will be deflected to the top of the scale, and this value of current is the f.s.d. current. We are referring here to the moving coil itself, that is the basic meter movement. This coil will have a certain resistance and therefore the voltage to cause f.s.d. can be calculated. Typical meter movements require $50\,\mu A$ for full-scale deflection and may be labelled:

$$\text{f.s.d.} = 50\,\mu A, \quad 10\,mV$$
$$R = 200\,\Omega$$

RANGE _____

By adding resistors *external* to the basic movement it may be converted to an ammeter or voltmeter of almost any required range. To make it into an ammeter resistors are placed in parallel with the moving coil, and for a voltmeter in series. By choosing suitable values meters can be designed to have almost any required range of measurement and f.s.d.

However, in all cases when the meter indicates full-scale it means that the current through the moving coil is the f.s.d. value of the basic movement.

For example, if the basic movement quoted above is used as the basis of a 10 V range voltmeter, it means that when 10 V exists across the terminal of the voltmeter a current of $50\,\mu A$ flows through the moving coil.

DISPLAY _____

The display of a meter depends upon its construction. The type of meter shown in Fig. 2.1 is called an *analogue instrument* because for a given current the needle will move through a certain angle. Thus current is represented by the angular movement of the needle. However, instead of marking the scale of the meter in degrees, it is marked to give the equivalent value of the current. Thus the operator must read the current value from the scale.

The alternative display is a *digital* display in which the value of the current is given directly as a numerical read out. (Compare wrist watches: the traditional type used the angle turned by the hands to represent time and thus were analogue instruments; the modern type uses numbers to give the time and are therefore digital instruments.)

ACCURACY

Accuracy of a measurement is best described in terms of the *errors* involved. There are two major groups of errors, *instrument errors* and *measurement errors.*

(i) *Instrument errors.* These are errors inherent in the instrument measuring system itself. This would depend on how well the meter itself is made, how good the bearings are and how uniform the magnetic field is. The accuracy is usually quoted as a percentage of full-scale deflection. For example, a 100 V range d.c. meter may be quoted as ± 2% f.s.d. This means that the maximum error anywhere on the scale would be 2% of 100 V or 2 V. If, therefore, the meter reads 80 V, the true reading could be between 78 V and 82 V giving an actual error of $\frac{2}{80} \times 100 = 2.5\%$. If on the other hand the reading is 10 V, the true reading could be anywhere between 8 V and 12 V. This gives an error of $\frac{2}{10} \times 100\% = 20\%$.

For this reason it is important that meter ranges are chosen such that the reading is above three-quarters of f.s.d.

Sometimes instead of writing ± 1% or ± 2% the meters are labelled Class 1.0 or Class 2.0 respectively.

Ultimately the reading on an *analogue* meter is obtained by observing the position of a pointer relative to a scale. The sub-division of the scale determines the *resolution* of the meter, and the accuracy to which this may be read constitutes a *reading error*. A common reading error is due to *parallax* because the observer's line of sight is not normal to the scale [see Fig. 2.5(a)]. To minimise parallax error meters have 'knife-blade' pointers and a mirror alongside the scale as shown in Fig. 2.5(b). The reading should only be taken when the pointer and its image coincide.

(ii) *Measurement errors.* These arise because the instrument used somehow alters the quantity being measured. For example, the current in a circuit may be 20 mA before the insertion of a milliammeter, but the meter may only read 19 mA. This may not be due to the meter being wrong, but because we are carrying out measurements not on the original circuit, but on a circuit modified by the presence of the meter. Such errors are dealt with in more detail later. Clearly such errors bring into question the *validity* of the measurement.

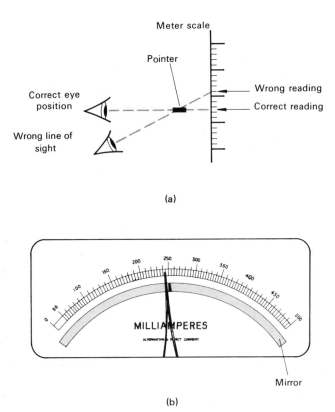

Fig. 2.5   (a) Parallax error, (b) how to eliminate it

VOLTMETERS AND AMMETERS

The moving-coil meter movement may be used as the basis of a voltmeter or ammeter. To convert it into a voltmeter a 'high' value *series* resistor, often called a *multiplier*, is connected in series with it. To make it into an ammeter a 'low' value *parallel* resistor, often called a *shunt* is connected in parallel with it. The situation is shown in Fig. 2.6.

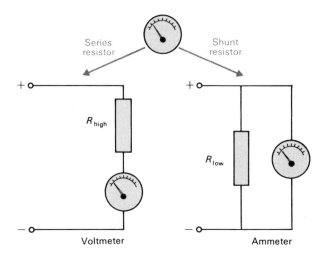

Fig. 2.6   Converting a moving-coil movement into a voltmeter or ammeter

VOLTMETERS

A basic movement having an f.s.d. of $50\,\mu$A can be converted into a voltmeter to read say $10\,$V by connecting a resistor R_s in series with it, as shown in Fig. 2.7.

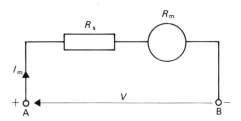

Fig. 2.7   Calculating R_s for a voltmeter

The total resistance between A and B must be such that when

$$V = 10\,\text{V}, \qquad I_\text{m} = 50\,\mu\text{A}$$

so

$$R_s + R_\text{m} = \frac{10\,\text{V}}{50\,\mu\text{A}} = 200\,000\,\Omega = 200\,\text{k}\Omega$$

and

$$R_s = 200\,\text{k}\Omega - R_\text{m}$$

the meter resistance will usually be less than $1\,\text{k}\Omega$ so the series resistor will be of the order of $200\,\text{k}\Omega$ – a relatively high value.

OHMS PER VOLT

A d.c. voltmeter may often be labelled as 20 000 ohms/volt. This figure enables the total resistance between the voltmeter terminals to be calculated easily. For example, on a 10 V range the total resistance will be $(10 \times 20\,000)\,\Omega = 200\,\text{k}\Omega$. The f.s.d. current can also be calculated. For example, in this case it will be $10\,\text{V} \div 200\,\text{k}\Omega = 50\,\mu\text{A}$, or more simply it *is the reciprocal of the ohms/volt value*; that is,

$$I_{\text{f.s.d.}} = \frac{1\,\text{V}}{20\,000\,\Omega} = 50\,\mu\text{A}$$

A *high* ohms/volt voltmeter will, therefore, take *less* current than a lower value, and generally meters of high Ω/V are to be preferred.

WORKED EXAMPLE 1

Show how a meter movement of f.s.d. $200\,\mu\text{A}$ and of resistance $500\,\Omega$ can be used for a switched dual range voltmeter reading 50 V and 100 V. Calculate the value of any resistors required.

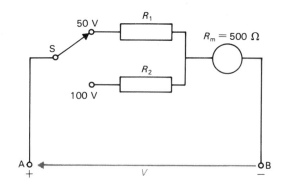

Fig. 2.8   Circuit for Worked Example 1

SOLUTION

The circuit is given in Fig. 2.8. With switch S in the 50 V position R_1 is in circuit, and we have

$$R_1 + R_m = \frac{50\,\text{V}}{200\,\mu\text{A}} = \frac{50\,\text{V}}{200 \times 10^{-6}\,\text{A}}$$

$$= \frac{50 \times 10^6}{200} = 250\,\text{K}$$

so
$$R_1 = 250\,\text{k}\Omega - 0.5\,\text{k}\Omega$$
$$= 249.5\,\text{k}\Omega$$

Similarly, for the 100 V position, we have

$$R_2 + R_m = \frac{100\,V}{200 \times 10^{-6}\,A} = 500\,k\Omega$$

so
$$R_2 = 499.5\,k\Omega$$

WORKED EXAMPLE 2

Two voltmeters have the following ranges and ohms/volt values. (a) State without making any calculations which will have the lowest f.s.d. current. (b) Calculate the f.s.d. current in each case. (c) Calculate the total resistance between the terminals of each voltmeter.

	Range	Ω/V
Voltmeter 1	200 V	1000
Voltmeter 2	20 V	10000

SOLUTION

(a)   Voltmeter 2 will have the lowest f.s.d. current as it has the highest ohms/volt value.

(b)   For voltmeter 1

$$I_{f.s.d.} = \frac{1\,V}{1000\,\Omega} = 1\,mA$$

For voltmeter 2

$$I_{f.s.d.} = \frac{1\,V}{10\,000\,\Omega} = 100\,\mu A$$

(c)   For voltmeter 1,   Total resistance $= 200 \times 1000 = 200\,k\Omega$

For voltmeter 2,   Total resistance $= 20 \times 10\,000 = 200\,k\Omega$

AMMETERS

A basic movement having an f.s.d. of $50\,\mu A$ may be converted into a milli-ammeter to read say 10 mA by connecting a resistor, or a 'shunt', R_s in parallel with it as shown in Fig. 2.9. Suppose that the f.s.d. voltage is 50 mV.

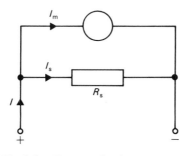

Fig. 2.9   The use of a shunt resistor to produce a milliammeter

The value of R_s may be calculated as follows:

We note that

$$I = I_s + I_m$$

If the meter is to read full-scale when $I = 10\,\text{mA}$ then $I_m = 50\,\mu\text{A}$, and so

$$I_s = I - I_m = 10\,\text{mA} - 50\,\mu\text{A} = 9.950\,\text{mA}$$

The voltage across the meter is the same as that across R_s, so that if the f.s.d is 50 mV, then

$$R_s = \frac{V_{\text{f.s.d.}}}{9.950\,\text{mA}}$$

$$R_s = \frac{50\,\text{mV}}{9.950\,\text{mA}} = 5.025\,\Omega$$

which is a low value compared with the meter resistance which will be $50\,\text{mV}/50\,\mu\text{A} = 1\,\text{k}\Omega$. R_s must be low compared to R_m since most of the current must pass through R_s.

An alternative method of finding R_s is to note that

$$\frac{I_m}{I_s} = \frac{R_s}{R_m}$$

so

$$R_s = R_m \frac{I_m}{I_s} = 1\,\text{k}\Omega \times \frac{50\,\mu\text{A}}{9.950\,\text{mA}}$$

$$= 10^3 \times \frac{50 \times 10^{-6}}{9.950 \times 10^{-3}} = \frac{50}{9.950}\,\Omega \quad \text{as before.}$$

WORKED EXAMPLE 3

A meter movement is labelled 15 mA, 75 mV, 5 Ω. Calculate the value of shunt resistance required to convert this into an ammeter to read 10 A.

SOLUTION

The circuit is shown as in Fig. 2.9. In this case

$$I_s = 10\,\text{A} - 15\,\text{mA} = 9.985\,\text{A}$$

So

$$\frac{R_s}{R_m} = \frac{I_m}{I_s} = \frac{0.015}{9.985}$$

So

$$R_s = \frac{0.015}{9.985} \times 5 = 0.0075\,\Omega$$

which is a very low value of resistance.

OHMMETERS

The value of resistance can always be calculated if the value of the voltage across and current through the resistor is known. However, for convenience, it is useful to have a direct reading meter for resistance. The principle is very simple. If a 10 V voltmeter is connected to a 10 V battery, it will read 10 V full-scale as shown in Fig. 2.10(a).

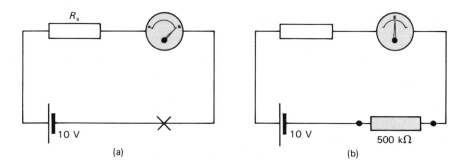

(a)   (b)

Fig. 2.10   The principle of an ohmmeter

Suppose the total resistance of the meter circuit is $500\,k\Omega$ as it was worked in Example 1. If now a $500\,k\Omega$ resistor was inserted at X as in Fig. 2.10(b), the meter would read 5 V, i.e. half-scale since the current will be halved because the total resistance has been doubled. A resistor less than $500\,k\Omega$ will cause a greater deflection than 5 V, whilst a larger resistor will give a smaller deflection.

The scale of the meter can be calibrated to read directly the value of the resistor connected at X.

In practice the battery is incorporated inside the case of the ohmmeter, and a variable resistor is used for 'zero-setting' as shown in Fig. 2.11(a). This resistor compensates for the decrease in battery voltage with time. The procedure for resistance measurement is as follows.

The meter terminals are connected together (short-circuited) by a piece of wire. The variable resistor R_V is adjusted until the meter is at full-scale. This is the zero of the resistance scale, and indicates the zero resistance now between the terminals. The unknown resistance is then connected between the terminals. The reading will be less than full scale and will depend on the value of R_X. This value is indicated directly on the scale.

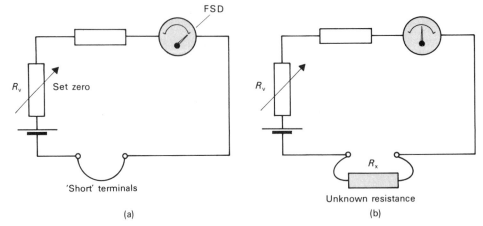

Fig. 2.11   The ohmmeter showing 'set zero' resistor: (a) with terminals shorted, (b) measuring an unknown resistance

The resistance scale is, therefore, reversed, zero being at the full-scale point. The scale is also non-linear and becomes extremely cramped at the high value end as seen in Fig. 2.12.

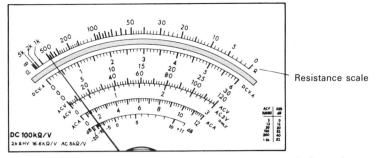

Fig. 2.12   A non-linear scale for resistance

The accuracy of resistance measurement by this means is not very great, and for better accuracy a voltage-divider principle may be used. For high-accuracy resistance measurements other methods are available. In most of these the unknown resistance is compared with a *standard* resistor and a meter is used only to indicate null conditions. In this way the accuracy of the meter is immaterial provided it is sensitive enough.

WORKED EXAMPLE 4

A simple ohmmeter circuit and scale are shown in Fig. 2.13. The meter movement is 100 μA, battery voltage 1.5 V. The value of R_1 may be adjusted to give f.s.d. when the terminals are short circuited. Calculate: (a) the total series resistance in the meter circuit when $R_x = 0$, (b) the resistance values on the meter scale corresponding to $\frac{1}{4}, \frac{1}{2}, \frac{3}{4}$ of full-scale.

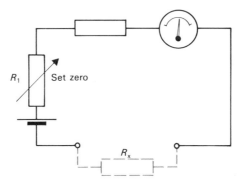

Fig. 2.13   Information for Worked Example 4

SOLUTION

(a)
$$R_{\text{total}} = \frac{1.5\,\text{V}}{100\,\mu\text{A}} = \frac{1.5\,\text{V}}{100 \times 10^{-6}\,\text{A}} = 15\,\text{k}\Omega$$

(b) The current in the circuit when an unknown resistance R_x is connected to the meter terminals will be

$$I = \frac{1.5\,\text{V}}{15\,\text{k}\Omega + R_x}$$

If we observe that the full-scale deflection is given by $1.5\,\text{V} \div 15\,\text{k}\Omega$ then by inspection from the above equation it can be seen that:

(i) when $R_x = 15\,\text{k}\Omega$ I will be one-half full-scale;

(ii) for I to be one-quarter full-scale requires the total resistance to be twice the value in (a), i.e. $60\,\text{k}\Omega$ so $R_x = 45\,\text{k}\Omega$;

(iii) for I to be three-quarters full scale, the total resistance should be one third the value in (b), i.e. $20\,\text{k}\Omega$ so $R_x = 5\,\text{k}\Omega$.

Summarising, we have

I (μA)	0	25	50	75	100
R_x (kΩ)	∞	45	15	5	0

These points are shown on the scale in Fig. 2.14.

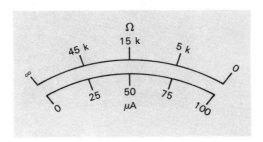

Fig. 2.14   The scales for the ohmmeter in Worked Example 4

MULTIMETERS

ANALOGUE MULTIMETERS

It is convenient and useful to combine the functions of a voltmeter, ammeter and ohmmeter in one instrument. Such meters are known as *multimeters*. The same moving-coil movement is, of course, used for all measurements, and a series of scales are provided to deal with the range of measurements. Normally there are several voltage, current and resistance ranges and provision to measure either d.c. or a.c. voltages. The selection of the measurement range required can take one of two forms, as follows.

TYPE 1

One or two rotary switches are used which can be switched to the range and function of measurement required. The meter leads are connected to two terminals or sockets on the meter and these terminals are used for all measurements except perhaps any particularly high voltage or current range. An example of such a meter is shown in Fig. 2.15.

Fig. 2.15   A multirange meter set to its 5 V range

TYPE 2

Instead of using a rotary switch this type uses a series of terminals or sockets. The pair of leads are connected to the terminals or sockets appropriate for the required measurement. An example of this type of multimeter is shown in Fig. 2.16.

Fig. 2.16   A multimeter using different terminals

Frequently instead of using the designation d.c. and a.c. on meters the following symbols are used:

DIGITAL MULTIMETERS

The meters described above are known as *analogue* meters since they display the measurement on an analogue scale. Another type is the *digital* multimeter which displays the measurement as a digital read-out, examples are seen in Fig. 2.17. Digital meters usually have greater accuracy and better resolution than analogue types. The polarity of the measurement is also automatically shown. Some digital meters have an *auto-ranging facility*. This means that the most suitable range for a measurement is automatically selected, although the *function* has to be manually selected.

Fig. 2.17   Digital multimeters

USING MULTIMETERS

SAFETY

Connection between the meter and circuit for which measurements are required is usually made by a pair of *test leads*. These are usually terminated in *crocodile clips* which can be attached to a part of a circuit, or in *test prods* which can be held on to any required points on the circuit. For safety it is essential to ensure the following:

(a)   test leads should be in good condition;

(b)   insulation not worn on any part;

(c)   insulation of the test prods should be adequate for voltage on which they are used — be particularly careful if measuring voltages over 100 V using a test prod in each hand;

(d)   test leads should be safely secured at the meter end so that there is no danger of them coming loose during use;

(e)   ensure that the meter case is not broken with the possibility of exposing any part of its circuit.

MEASURING VOLTAGE AND CURRENT

The following procedures should be followed:

(a)   Check that the pointer is on the zero of the scale. If not, set to zero by means of the adjustment screw provided. (For digital meters check on manufacturer's instruction for calibration.)

(b)   Select the function required — current or voltage, a.c. or d.c.

(c)   Observe the polarity and select a range that is considerably greater than the higher value of measurement you expect. Even if the polarity is wrong, this would ensure that the meter is not given a large impulse in the wrong direction.

(*Note*. On some meters a trip facility exists which turns the meter off if the input current or voltage is too high. If the instrument is not recording, you should check to see if the trip has operated. Some meters also have a reverse polarity button which is useful if the leads have been connected the wrong way round and the pointer is deflected against the stop. By pressing this button the meter will give a reading.)

(d)   Reduce the range selected until the reading is in the top third of the scale.

(*Note*. When changing range on a multimeter, remember that you are changing the resistance the meter presents to the circuit and this itself can result in discrepancies in the readings between two ranges. For example, on a 100 V range a meter may read 30 V, but when switched to a 30 V range the reading may be only 28 V. Both readings may be correct under the conditions the measurements are made!)

(e)   Use the most appropriate scale on the meter for the range you have selected, and use the scale mirror to eliminate any parallax error.

MEASURING RESISTANCE

(a)   Switch to the resistance function and select the appropriate resistance range.

(b)   Connect the test prods together to provide a short circuit and use the '*ohms set zero*' control to set the pointer to zero on the resistance scale (usually at full-scale deflection).

(c) Connect the unknown resistance between the ends of the test leads and note resistance measurement on scale. If possible select a range that gives a reading around mid-scale.

(*Note.* Do not attempt any resistance measurements on circuits that are energised. Ensure that all voltage supplies are removed or switched off before resistance measurements are made on the circuit.)

THE USE OF INSTRUMENTS IN PRACTICAL WORK _____

For the practical work discussed below, conventional voltmeters or ammeters may be used. Multimeters can also be used throughout. In all cases the effect of the resistance of the meter on the circuit must be considered.

An electronic (high-impedance) voltmeter should be available so that its readings can be compared with those taken on the conventional meters.

SERIES CIRCUITS _____

Fig. 2.18 shows a simple two-resistor series network. With the values shown in the diagram,

$$I = \frac{V}{R_1 + R_2} = \frac{12}{18} = \frac{2}{3}\text{A}$$

$$V_1 = IR_1 = \frac{2}{3} \times 6 = 4\text{ V}$$

$$V_2 = IR_2 = \frac{2}{3} \times 12 = 8\text{ V}$$

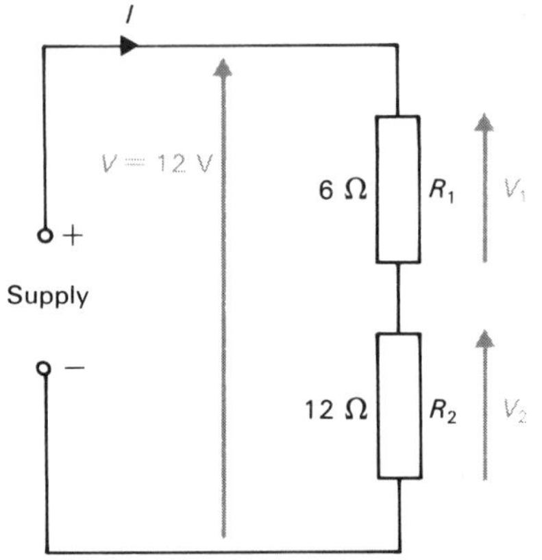

Fig. 2.18   A series circuit

As a practical exercise set up a similar circuit with R_1 and R_2 less than $100\,\Omega$. Calculate the values of I, V_1 and V_2 as shown above. Then connect in the measuring instruments (see Fig. 2.19) to measure I, V, V_1 and V_2. Show that

$$V = V_1 + V_2$$

$$I = \frac{V}{R_1 + R_2}$$

$$V_1 = IR_1$$

and $$V_2 = IR_2$$

Note that in Fig. 2.19 the ammeter is connected in series in the circuit and that the voltmeters are connected in parallel.

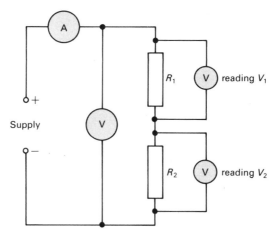

Fig. 2.19 Meters in a series circuit

Repeat the experiment using higher values for R_1 and R_2. As your resistance values increase you may find discrepancies in your results.

For example, suppose that you have a circuit similar to the one shown in Fig. 2.20. Then

$$I = \frac{V}{R_1 + R_2} = \frac{12}{150\,k\Omega} = 0.08\,mA = 80\,\mu A$$

$$V_1 = IR_1 = 0.08\,mA \times 100\,k\Omega = 8\,V$$

$$V_2 = IR_2 = 0.08\,mA \times 50\,k\Omega = 4\,V$$

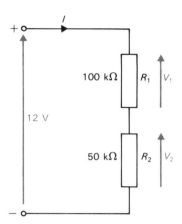

Fig. 2.20   A series circuit using high resistances

The voltages obtained in the above calculation are those which would be obtained using an *ideal* voltmeter — that is, one with such a high resistance that it would not effectively alter the circuit when connected into it. (Modern electronic voltmeters fall into this category since they have resistance of 10 MΩ or more.)

Suppose the voltmeter used is 'non-ideal' and that it has a resistance of 200 kΩ. Fig. 2.21(a) shows the circuit used to observe V_1. The voltmeter *measures the voltage across the combination of 100 kΩ and 200 kΩ in parallel.* The equivalent resistance R_3 of this combination is given by

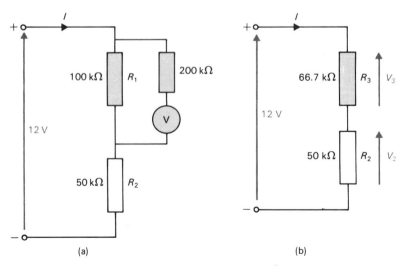

Fig. 2.21   (a) Voltage measurement using a 'non-ideal' voltmeter, and (b) its equivalent circuit

$$\frac{1}{R_3} = \frac{1}{100\,\text{k}\Omega} + \frac{1}{200\,\text{k}\Omega} = \frac{3}{200\,\text{k}\Omega}$$

$$R_3 = \frac{200}{3} = 66.7\,\text{k}\Omega$$

The equivalent circuit is shown in Fig. 2.21(b). Thus

$$I = \frac{12}{R_2 + R_3} = \frac{12}{116.7\,\text{k}\Omega} = 0.103\,\text{mA}$$

$$V_3 = IR_3 = 0.103\,\text{mA} \times 66.7\,\text{k}\Omega = 6.87\,\text{V}$$

Note that the current increases from 0.08 mA to 0.103 mA and that V_3 *is smaller than the value of* V_1 which equals 8 V, V_1 being the voltage which would be obtained using an ideal voltmeter. (As an exercise calculate the voltage recorded across R_2 using the voltmeter with a resistance of 200 kΩ.)

An ideal voltmeter is therefore one which has an infinite resistance so that it does not change the current in the circuit into which it is connected.

An ideal ammeter should have zero resistance so that it does not reduce the current in the circuit into which it is connected.

When conducting an experiment you should check throughout that your instruments do not appreciably alter the circuit in which they are used to take measurements.

SERIES-PARALLEL CIRCUITS

Fig. 2.22(a) shows a simple series–parallel resistor network. The two resistors in parallel have an effective resistance R_4 given by

$$\frac{1}{R_4} = \frac{1}{R_2} + \frac{1}{R_3} = \frac{1}{30} + \frac{1}{20} = \frac{5}{60} = \frac{1}{12}$$

$$R_4 = 12\,\Omega$$

The equivalent circuit is shown in Fig. 2.22(b). Thus

$$I = \frac{V}{R_1 + R_4} = \frac{12}{22} = 0.545\,\text{A}$$

$$V_1 = IR_1 = 5.45\,\text{V}$$

$$V_4 = IR_4 = 6.55\,\text{V}$$

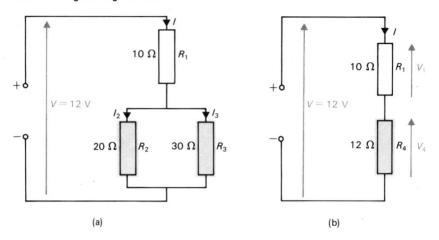

Fig. 2.22   (a) A series-parallel circuit. (b) Its equivalent circuit

Referring to Fig. 2.22 shows that

$$I_2 = \frac{V_4}{R_2} = 0.327\,\text{A}$$

$$I_3 = \frac{V_4}{R_3} = 0.218\,\text{A}$$

Note that $V = V_1 + V_4$ and $I = I_2 + I_3$.

Now try this experiment. Set up a circuit similar to that shown in Fig. 2.22. Make your resistance values less than $100\,\Omega$. Use the relevant meters to measure I, I_2, I_3, V, V_1 and V_4. Check that your results agree with your calculations.

Now repeat the experiment using higher resistance values and check each time to see how the meter resistances affect the circuit.

OBTAINING A VARIABLE VOLTAGE D.C. SUPPLY _____

For many laboratory experiments and engineering applications it is necessary to have a variable d.c. voltage.

Although special power units with a variable output may be purchased, for many applications a simple *potential divider* may be used. The principle is shown in Fig. 2.23.

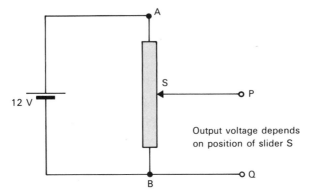

Fig. 2.23   A variable voltage d.c. supply

Resistance wire is uniformly wound on a tube and its two ends A and B are connected to a battery. A movable contact S (slider) can make contact with the wire at any point. When S is at the top end, the voltage between P and Q will be 12 V. When S is at the bottom end the output voltage at PQ will be zero. Hence by varying the position of S the output voltage can be varied between 0 and the full voltage of the supply.

Provided no current is taken from the output, the output voltage will be proportional to the 'distance' the slider S is from B.

The device can take one of several forms:

(a)   If the resistance is wound on a straight tube it is called a *linear rheostat*.

(b)   The resistance wire can be wound on a former bent into the arc of a circle and the slider S connected to a rotational spindle.

(c)   The resistance element can be a carbon strip in the form of a circular arc. These are often used as volume controls in radios, and commonly called *pots.*

(d)   For precision work the wire may be wound in a helix on the inside of a small cylinder, and again contact made by a rotating spindle. These are called *helical potentiometers* or simply *helipots.*

EXERCISE 2

Multi-choice questions

1)   Which of the following is *not* an essential part of a moving-coil meter?

a a pivoted coil   b a spiral hairspring

c a non-parallax mirror   d a linear scale

2) A moving-coil meter reads half-scale. The reading could be increased when connected to the same circuit by:

a decreasing the 'stiffness' of the controlling spring

b decreasing the magnetic field in the air gap

c increasing the resistance of the moving coil

d increasing the 'stiffness' of the controlling spring

3) A student describing the construction of a moving-coil meter uses the following words. Which description is not appropriate?

a pivoted coil   b non-parallax mirror

c non-linear scale   d copper wire

4) The f.s.d. value of a moving-coil movement:

a is the current required to give maximum deflection of the pointer

b is the same value for all microammeters

c is dependant on whether the meter is used as a voltmeter or ammeter

d is dependant on the value of the external shunt resistance

5) The current through the shunt of an ammeter will always be:

a less than the current through the meter movement

b a constant fraction of the current through the meter movement

c a constant value irrespective of the current through the meter movement

d a minimum when the current through the meter movement is a maximum

6) The 'ohms per volt' value of a voltmeter:

a can be used to calculate the resistance of the moving coil

b can be used to calculate the total meter resistance on a specified range

c depends on the voltage the meter is indicating

d depends on the resistance of the circuit under test

7) A meter is stated to be $10\,000\,\Omega/V$. Its f.s.d. current will be:

a 1 mA   b 10 mA   c $100\,\mu A$ d $10\,\mu A$

8) The f.s.d. of a meter is stated to be 0.5 mA. Its 'ohms per volt' value will be:

   a 5000   b 2000   c 1000   d 200

9) The scale of a ohmmeter reads backwards because:

   a it is non-linear

   b the current through the coil is reversed

   c f.s.d. indicates zero external resistance

   d none of the above

10) An ideal voltmeter will have:

   a zero resistance   b infinite resistance

   c low resistance   d high resistance

11) An ideal ammeter will have:

   a zero resistance   b infinite resistance

   c low resistance   d high resistance

12) A meter movement has a resistance of $100\,\Omega$ and an f.s.d. of $1\,mA$. To convert it to an ammeter reading $1\,A$ full scale would require a shunt resistor:

   a greater than $100\,\Omega$ b of approximately $10\,\Omega$

   c of approximately $1\,\Omega$ d of approximately $0.1\,\Omega$

13) A meter movement has a resistance of $200\,\Omega$ and f.s.d. $10\,\mu A$. To convert it to a voltmeter reading $10\,V$ would require a series resistor of approximately:

   a $1\,M\Omega$ b $100\,k\Omega$ c $1\,k\Omega$ d $200\,\Omega$

Problems

14) A voltmeter is labelled as Class 2 accuracy. It is used to measure a voltage of 80 V. What would be the range of likely readings if the meter is used: (a) on its 100 V range, (b) on its 200 V range.

15) A meter movement is labelled $50\,\Omega$, $1\,mA$ f.s.d. This movement is used in an ammeter with a shunt resistance of $1\,\Omega$.

(a) Draw the circuit of the complete ammeter.

(b) When the meter indicates half-scale deflection:
     (i) what current flows through the meter?
     (ii) what current flows through the shunt?

(c) What is the total current flowing through the ammeter (i.e. shunt and and meter movement) when the meter indicates f.s.d?

16) A meter movement of $2000\,\Omega$, $100\,\mu A$ f.s.d. is used in a voltmeter. (a) Draw the circuit of the complete instrument. (b) If the series resistor is $98\,k\Omega$ what voltage should be marked at (i) half-scale, (ii) full-scale?

17) A meter movement of $1000\,\Omega$, $100\,\mu A$ f.s.d. is to be used for a dual range voltmeter as shown in Fig. 2.8. Calculate the values of R_1 and R_2 if the meter is to read full scale for $100\,V$ and $25\,V$ in the switch positions A and B respectively.

18) A meter movement of $50\,\Omega$, $1\,mA$ f.s.d. is to be converted into an ammeter reading $1\,A$ full-scale. Draw the circuit of the arrangement and calculate the values of any components required.

19) Fig. 2.24 shows the circuit of a multirange milliammeter. Calculate the values of R_1, R_2 and R_3. This milliammeter when switched to the $100\,mA$ range is connected to a circuit. The current indicated is less than $10\,mA$. What would be the danger of using the switch as shown to change to the $10\,mA$ range? How can this problem be overcome?

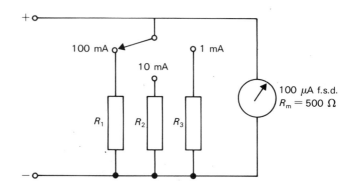

Fig. 2.24

20)   The circuit shown in Fig. 2.25 is to be used as an ammeter. Calculate the value of the current I that will produce full-scale deflection of the meter.

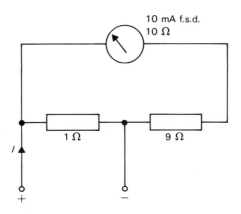

Fig. 2.25

21)   (a) Calculate the voltages V_{AB} and V_{BC} for the circuit of Fig. 2.26.

   (b) If a voltmeter of 10 000 ohms/volt is used on its 10 V range to measure these voltages what will it read when connected across (i) A and B, (ii) B and C?

   (c) Determine the actual ratio of the voltages V_{AB} and V_{BC} as calculated in (a) and compare this with the ratio of the voltmeter readings.

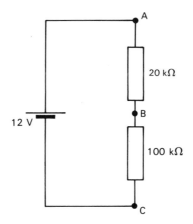

Fig. 2.26

22) Fig. 2.27 shows a circuit representing the headlights and starter motor of a motor car. Indicate where you would connect: (a) an ammeter to indicate the current taken by the lights, (b) a voltmeter to measure the battery voltage.

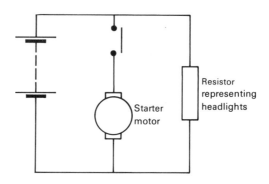

Fig. 2.27

23) For the circuit of Fig. 2.28 show where you would connect: (a) ammeters to measure the current through R_1 and through R_3, (b) a voltmeter to measure the voltage across R_3.

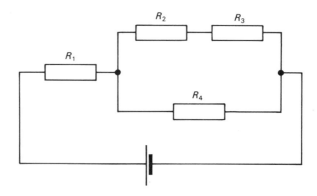

Fig. 2.28

24) The armature resistance of a d.c. motor is thought to be less than $1\,\Omega$. An attempt is made to measure this by a voltmeter and ammeter using the circuit of Fig. 2.29. The voltmeter reading is 12 V and the ammeter reads 10 A. This appears to give a resistance value in excess of $1\,\Omega$. Why? Can you suggest a modification to the circuit that would give a more accurate answer?

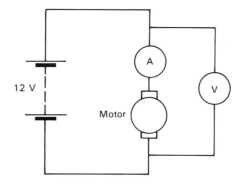

Fig. 2.29

ELECTROMAGNETISM

After reaching the end of this chapter you should be able to:

1. *Define the terms magnetic flux and magnetic flux density.*
2. *Sketch magnetic fields due to simple arrangements of magnets and current-carrying conductors.*
3. *State the factors that determine the force on a current-carrying conductor in a magnetic field and calculate the force in simple cases.*
4. *Use simple rules to determine the direction of electromagnetic forces.*
5. *Explain the action of a simple d.c. motor.*
6. *State and illustrate experimentally the laws of electromagnetic induction.*
7. *Describe the phenomenon of mutual induction.*
8. *Describe the action of a simple generator and sketch the generated voltage waveform.*
9. *Calculate the generated voltage in simple cases of 'flux cutting' and 'flux linking' situations.*
10. *Describe the action of a transformer and solve simple problems involving voltage and current ratios.*

MAGNETIC FIELDS

THE CONCEPT OF A MAGNETIC FIELD

It is well known that the 'needle' of a magnetic compass will be deflected if a bar magnet is brought near to it. In some way the magnet exerts a force on the needle, and this force takes place without any physical contact between the magnet and the needle.

To explain this phenomena we say that the bar magnet produces a magnetic field in the space around it, and it is this field that in some way causes the needle to deflect.

To represent magnetic fields in diagrams we use lines, with an arrow for indicating direction. This is similar to using lines to represent rays of light. The magnetic field produced by a bar magnet is shown in Fig. 3.1. The direction of the field is the direction in which a magnetic compass needle points.

It is sometimes convenient to identify the ends of a magnet as N (for north) and S (for south). If a bar magnet was suspended about its mid-point, the N-end would point to the magnetic north. It is thus seen that:

(a)   magnetic field lines leave the N-end and enter the S-end of a bar magnet,

(b)   the magnetic field lines form continuous loops which pass through the magnet.

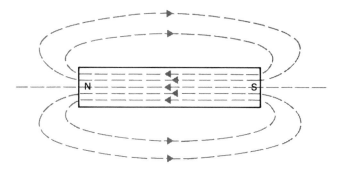

Fig. 3.1   The magnetic field of a bar magnet

Other magnetic field patterns are shown in Fig. 3.2. It should be remembered that the magnetic field lines do form continuous loops although this is not always shown.

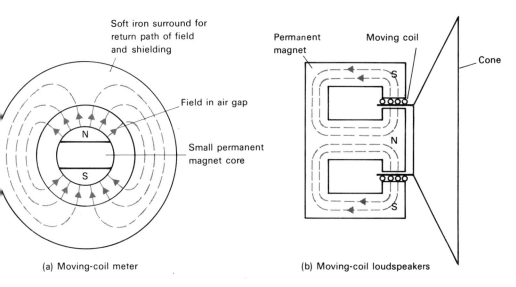

(a) Moving-coil meter   (b) Moving-coil loudspeakers

Fig. 3.2 (continued overleaf)

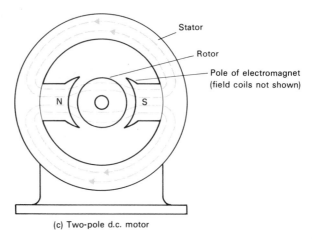

(c) Two-pole d.c. motor

Fig. 3.2   Magnetic field patterns

FIELDS FROM CURRENT

A magnetic field can also be produced by an electric current. If for example an electric current is passed through a cylindrical coil about the size of a bar magnet (Fig. 3.3), the pattern of the magnetic field produced is very similar in both cases.

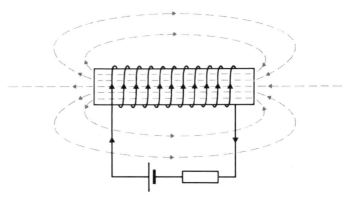

Fig. 3.3   The magnetic field produced by a current in a coil wound on a cardboard tube (solenoid)

The pattern of such fields can be found experimentally by using a magnetic compass or iron filings. If this is done for a straight wire or conductor carrying a current, it will be found that the magnetic field forms a series of concentric circles as shown in Fig. 3.4.

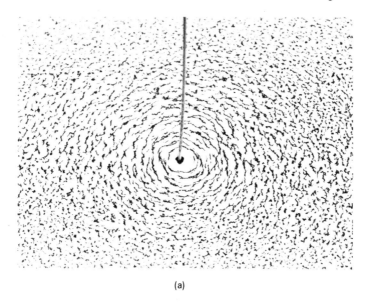

(a)

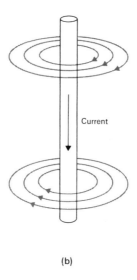

Current

(b)

Fig. 3.4   (a) Iron filings show circular pattern of field due to current in wire
(b) Concentric magnetic field due to current in a straight conductor

An interesting pattern is the magnetic field produced by a coil wound on a circular tube – known as a *toroidal coil* or *toroid*. This is shown in Fig. 3.5, and it should be noted that the field is entirely within the coil and is uniform as shown by the magnetic field lines being equally spaced.

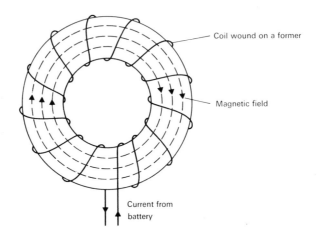

Fig. 3.5   The magnetic field produced by a toroid

Since, as we have said, the magnetic field lines always form closed loops, we often refer to a magnetic circuit. A magnetic circuit is a system which produces a magnetic field, the system being analogous to an electric circuit which produces current. The concept of a closed path or continuity exists in both cases. Furthermore it is important to note that electric circuits and magnetic circuits link each other as shown in Fig. 3.6.

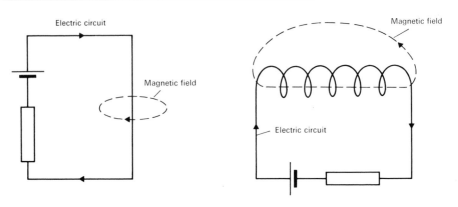

Fig. 3.6   Electric circuits and magnetic fields always link each other as can be seen in these two examples

RULE FOR FINDING THE DIRECTION OF THE MAGNETIC FIELD _____

For a straight conductor the direction of the magnetic field produced by a current in it can be found easily as follows.

Imagine you are holding the wire in your right hand as shown in Fig. 3.7. Point your thumb in the direction of the current, your fingers will curl around in the direction of the magnetic field.

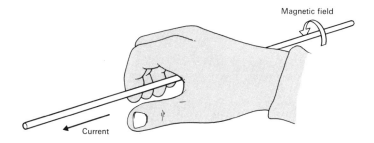

Fig. 3.7   Finding the direction of magnetic field due to a straight conductor

This can be adapted for a coil as shown in Fig. 3.8. Grasp the coil so that this time your fingers point in the direction of the current in each turn of the coil, then your thumb will point in the direction of the magnetic field.

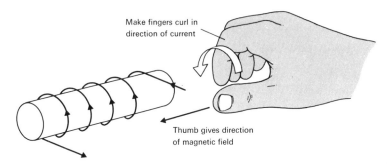

Fig. 3.8   Finding the direction of the magnetic field in a coil

An adaption of this rule is the *right-hand corkscrew rule*. If a corkscrew is pointed in the direction of the current in a wire as shown in Fig. 3.9, then the direction in which a corkscrew is normally turned (clockwise) will give the direction of the magnetic field. It is left for you to work out how this rule can be adapted for a coil.

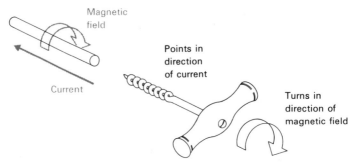

Fig. 3.9   The 'corkscrew' rule

The student should now apply these rules to Figs. 3.3, 3.4(b) and 3.5 to confirm that the magnetic field directions are shown correctly.

An important point to note is that if the current direction is reversed, then the direction of the magnetic field is reversed.

MAGNETIC FLUX (Φ) AND FLUX DENSITY (B)

Although we cannot 'see' magnetism, it is convenient to image that the magnetic field produces something that is real and whose influence can be detected. This we call *magnetic flux.* The symbol for magnetic flux is the Greek capital letter phi (Φ), and its unit is the *Weber* (Wb). Wherever a magnetic field exists there will be a magnetic flux, so it is quite convenient to think of the magnetic field lines we have drawn also representing magnetic flux.

The magnetic flux is the total quantity of 'magnetic field lines' in a magnetic circuit, and what is important in many cases is not this total quantity but how it is distributed, or in other words, its *density.* We also have to consider over what area the flux is spread. The area is taken as perpendicular to the direction of the flux, and this *magnetic flux density* is defined as *magnetic flux per unit area.* The unit is Weber per square meter (Wb/m^2) which is given the name of Tesla (T). The symbol for magnetic flux density is B.

Hence
$$B = \frac{\Phi}{A}$$
[3.1]

The value of B in magnetic circuits made of iron with small air gaps is usually in the range 1 T to 2 T.

The situation is summarised in Fig. 3.10. The student will no doubt detect the similarity between this and the concepts force and stress in a mechanical system.

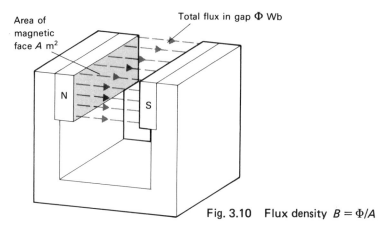

Area of magnetic face A m²

Total flux in gap Φ Wb

N

S

Fig. 3.10   Flux density $B = \Phi/A$

WORKED EXAMPLE 1

A student estimates that the magnetic flux in an iron toroid of the type shown in Fig. 3.5 is 2×10^{-3} Wb. If the cross-sectional area of the toroid is $2\,\text{cm}^2$, is the estimated value sensible?

SOLUTION

We test this by finding the value of the magnetic flux density to see if it falls within the possible range for iron, which is not likely to be greater than 2 T.

We have from equation [3.1]

$$\text{Flux density } B = \frac{\text{Flux }(\Phi)}{\text{Area }(A)}$$

$$= \frac{2 \times 10^{-3}\,\text{Wb}}{2 \times 10^{-4}\,\text{m}^2}$$

$$= 10\,\text{T}$$

This is not reasonable as it is far too great.

WORKED EXAMPLE 2

A current of 0.5 A produces a flux of 1×10^{-6} Wb in a toroidal coil which is air-cored, i.e. there is no iron present. If in such a case the flux produced is proportional to current, what current would be required for a flux density of 1×10^{-2} T? The cross-sectional area of the coil is $2\,\text{cm}^2$.

SOLUTION

For a flux density of 1×10^{-2} T, the total flux will be given by

$$\Phi = BA \quad \text{(from equation [3.1])}$$

$$= (1 \times 10^{-2}) \times (2 \times 10^{-4})\,\text{Wb}$$

$$= 2 \times 10^{-6}\,\text{Wb}$$

This is twice the flux produced by 0.5 A, so the required current is 1.0 A.

INTERACTION OF MAGNETIC FIELDS

The needle of a magnetic compass is itself a small magnet. As such it produces a magnetic field. This field interacts with the Earth's magnetic field and the result is that the needle points north. Similarly the needle can be made to deflect by having a bar magnet brought near it. These are two examples of magnetic fields interacting.

When two magnetic fields interact, the individual magnetic fields are modified to produce one resultant pattern. It is well known that if the S-ends of two bar magnets are brought near each other, there is a repulsion force between them. If an N-end of one and the S-end of another are brought near, they attract each other. The two situations are shown in Fig. 3.11.

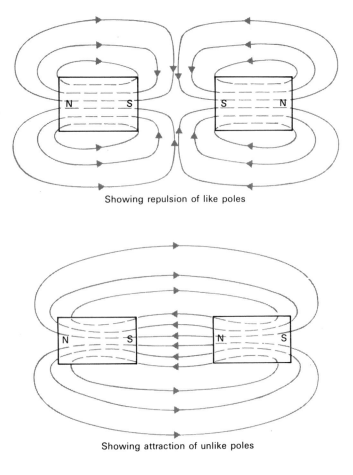

Showing repulsion of like poles

Showing attraction of unlike poles

Fig. 3.11   Magnetic field patterns between two bar magnets

The magnetic fields produced by current-carrying conductors may also interact. If two parallel conductors carry current in the same direction the field patterns are as in Fig. 3.12.

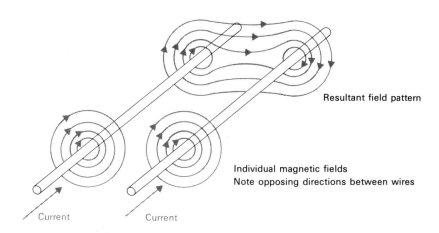

Resultant field pattern

Individual magnetic fields
Note opposing directions between wires

Current   Current

Fig. 3.12   Field due to current in two parallel conductors

In this case it is seen that the magnetic field lines weaken and cancel out between the conductors, but add and therefore strengthen the field on the outer sides. In such a case the result is that the conductors experience a force tending to push them together — that is, attract each other.

A similar analysis with currents in opposite directions will show that the field is strengthened between the conductors but weakened on the outside, and in such a case the conductors tend to be pushed apart — that is, repel each other.

The interaction of magnetic or electromagnetic forces have important industrial and commercial applications. Modern developments include the magnetic suspension of experimental trains such as that shown in Fig. 3.13.

Fig. 3.13   Magnetic suspension vehicle developed in Germany

ELECTROMAGNETIC FORCES _____

FINDING THE DIRECTION OF THE FORCE _____

If a conductor AB (Fig. 3.14) which carries a current is placed at right angles to a magnetic field produced by either a permanent or electromagnet, the conductor will experience a force. This, as in previous cases is due to the interaction between (a) the field due to the current in the conductor and (b) the other field. If free to move, the conductor will move as shown.

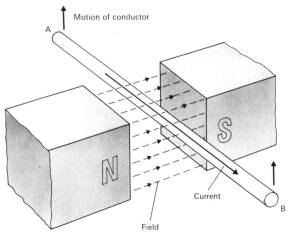

Fig. 3.14   Force on a current-carrying conductor placed in a magnetic field

The direction of motion can be found as follows. Fig. 3.15(a) shows a front view of the arrangement with both magnetic fields superimposed on each other. Fig. 3.15(b) shows the resultant field.

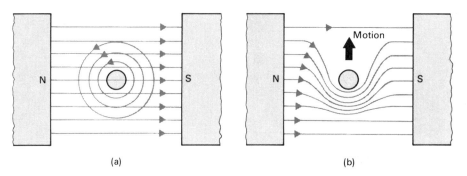

(a)   (b)

Fig. 3.15   Finding the direction of motion

The fields cancel above the conductor, but add below it. There is, therefore, a strengthening of the field below which we can think of as catapulting the conductor upwards.

FLEMING'S LEFT-HAND RULE

In Fig. 3.14 we have three quantities whose directions are at right angles, the magnetic field, the current, and the force or motion. These are shown in Fig. 3.16. By using the thumb and first two fingers of the *left hand* we can represent any two of these quantities and hence find the third. The rule is given below and illustrated in Fig. 3.17.

> Fleming's left-hand rule
>
> First finger points in direction of **F**ield
> se**C**ond finger points in direction of **C**urrent
> thu**M**b gives direction of **M**otion

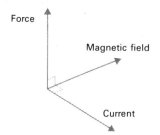

Fig. 3.16   The three quantities, current, field and force are mutually at right angles

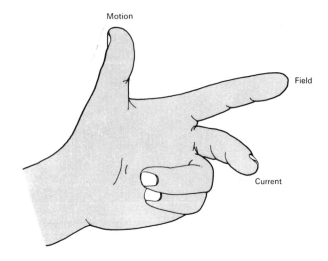

Fig. 3.17   Fleming's left-hand rule for finding direction of motion

The student should be satisfied that both rules stated above are consistent with each other and use whichever is preferred.

MAGNITUDE OF THE FORCE

If an experiment was conducted with the arrangement shown in Fig. 3.14, there are three quantities that can be changed and which we would expect to influence the force. They are:

(a)   the value of the current, I;

(b)   the magnetic flux density, B;

(c)   the length of conductor, L, *at right angles* to the magnetic field.

Let us consider these in turn.

(a)   If the current is doubled and everything else kept the same, it is found that the force is doubled. This is indicated in Fig. 3.18.

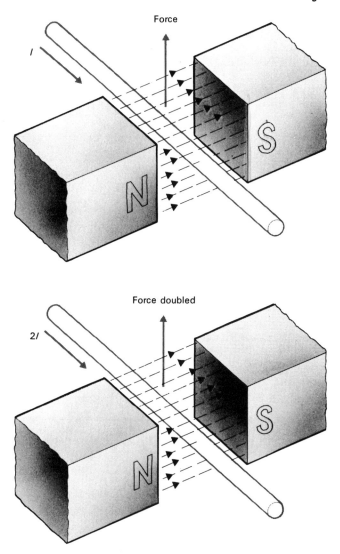

Fig. 3.18   The effect on the force when the current *I* is increased

(b)   If the magnetic flux density is doubled and everything else kept the same, it is found the force is doubled. This is indicated in Fig. 3.19.

(c)   If the length of conductor at right angles to the field is increased and everything else kept the same, it is found that the force is doubled. Note that we can do this as shown in Fig. 3.20 so that the flux density *B* does not change from the previous case.

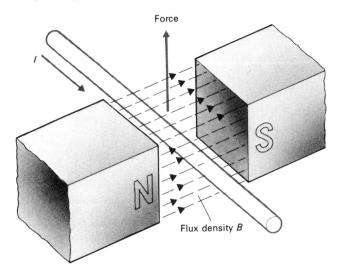

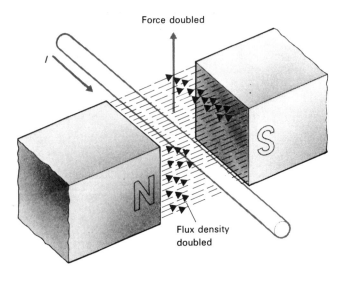

Fig. 3.19   The effect on the force when the flux density *B* is increased

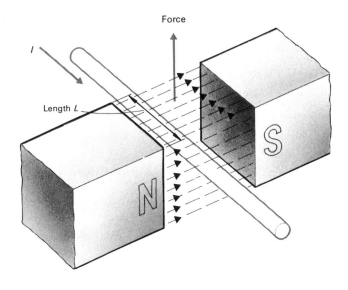

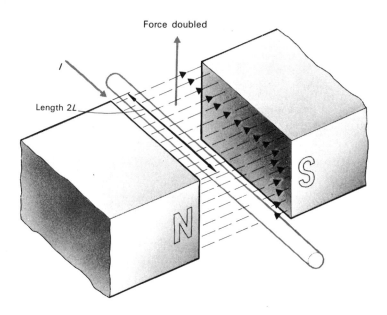

Fig. 3.20   The effect on the force when the length *L* is increased

It can, therefore, be concluded that:

The force on the conductor is proportional to:

(a)   the current I,

(b)   the magnetic flux density B,

(c)   the conductor length L;

or, in symbol form,

$$\text{Force,} \quad F \propto BLI$$

or, if suitable units are chosen,

$$F = BLI$$ [3.2]

where F = force in newtons

B = flux density in tesla

L = length in metres

I = current in amperes

Equation [3.2] has applications in both d.c. motors and d.c. meters (d.c. meters have been dealt with in Chapter 2).

WORKED EXAMPLE 3

Find the force on an arrangement such as Fig. 3.14 if the current is 10 A, the length of conductor 0.1 m, the flux 1×10^{-3} Wb and the dimensions of the magnetic pole faces are 10 cm $\times$ 2 cm.

SOLUTION

Step 1

Find the flux density B using equation [3.1].

The cross-sectional area A is $10 \times 2 \times 10^{-4}$ m²

$$B = \frac{\Phi}{A} = \frac{1 \times 10^{-3}}{2 \times 10^{-3}} \, \text{T}$$
$$B = 0.5 \, \text{T}$$

Step 2

Use $F = BLI$ (equation [3.2])

$$F = 0.5 \times 0.1 \times 10 \, \text{N}$$
$$F = 0.5 \, \text{N}$$

A SIMPLE D.C. MOTOR

The d.c. motor is based on the principle discussed in the previous section. In its simplest form it would consist of a one-turn coil having two sides P and Q as in Fig. 3.21.

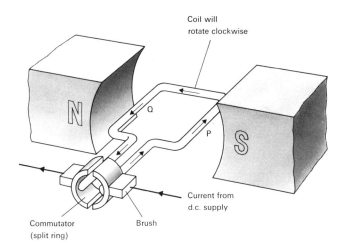

Fig. 3.21   The principle of the d.c. electric motor

The current from a d.c. supply or battery is fed to the coil via *carbon brushes* which make electrical contact with the *commutator*. The commutator, which rotates with the coil, has two half-segments insulated from each other. It ensures that whichever side of the coil is nearest the N-pole, say, the current will always be in the direction shown and hence the force will always be upwards. The stages that produce rotation are shown in Fig. 3.22. The direction of force on sides P and Q can be found by using Fleming's left-hand rule.

In order to produce as high a flux as possible the coil is wound on to an iron rotor and thus the air gap is very small.

In practice the coil will consist of many turns distributed around the rotor and there will be several commutator segments. This ensures that there is always some coils in the horizontal position which will produce maximum torque. A typical d.c. motor is shown in Fig. 3.23 (page 91).

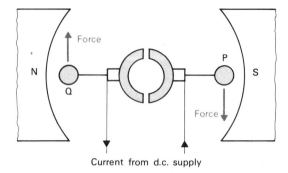

Current from d.c. supply

Force is up on Q and down on P producing clockwise motion

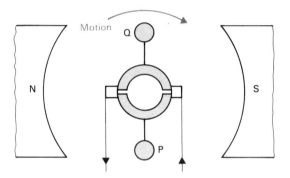

In this position the inertia of the system carries the coil forward

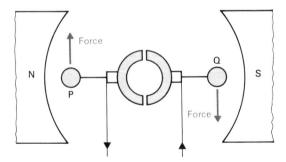

Although sides P and Q have now changed position the force still produces clockwise motion

Fig. 3.22   The action of the commutator

Fig. 3.23   A d.c. motor showing commutator and brushes

ELECTROMAGNETIC INDUCTION AND GENERATION _____

The basis of all large-scale electrical power generation today stems from Faraday's discovery of how to generate electricity by making use of the magnetic field.

A SIMPLE EXPERIMENT _____

It is easy to demonstrate how electricity may be generated using a magnetic field as follows.

Set up the circuit of Fig. 3.24 using a multimeter set to its lowest voltage or current range. Experiment to find which is best. (Alternatively a centre-zero microammeter is even better). A coil should be wound with several turns of wire, (the more the better) and its diameter large enough so that a bar magnet can be moved in and out of it. When this is done the following can be observed:

(a)   When the magnet is moved towards or into the coil, a deflection on the meter is seen, showing that a voltage is generated in the coil.

(b)   Moving the magnet away from the coil gives a deflection in the opposite direction (the multimeter will be observed to move against the stop).

(c) When the magnet and coil are stationary no voltage is generated, even if the magnet is inside the coil.

(d) A voltage can also be generated if the coil is moved towards or over the magnet.

(e) The more rapid the movement of the magnet or coil, the greater is the generated voltage.

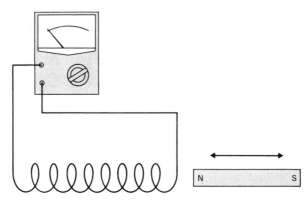

Fig. 3.24   A demonstration of electromagnetic generation. Moving the magnet in and out of the coil gives a deflection on the meter

The physical explanation of the above phenomena is that whenever there is *relative motion* between a magnetic field and an electrical conductor, a voltage is generated. In the above case, it should be noted that as the magnet is moved towards the coil, the magnetic flux linking or intersecting the coil increases as can be seen in Fig. 3.25. It is this *change of flux linkages* that is essential for the generation of a voltage.

The polarity of the generated voltage depends on which direction the magnet is moved, that is, on whether the flux linkages are increasing or decreasing.

Another demonstration of electromagnetic generation may be made by moving a conductor between the poles of a magnet (Fig. 3.26). The following can be observed if a sensitive meter is connected across AB:

(a) When the conductor AB is moved downwards through the magnetic field a voltage is generated. If moved upwards through the field, the generated voltage is in the opposite direction.

(b) The faster AB is moved in a vertical direction the greater the voltage.

(c) If conductor AB is moved horizontally from left to right, or right to left, even if it is well within the magnetic field, no generated voltage is observed.

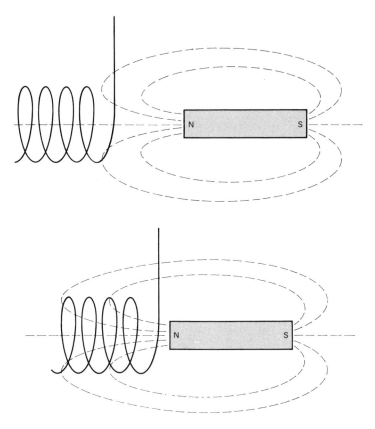

Fig. 3.25   A change of magnetic linkages with a coil. When the magnet is brought nearer there are more linkages

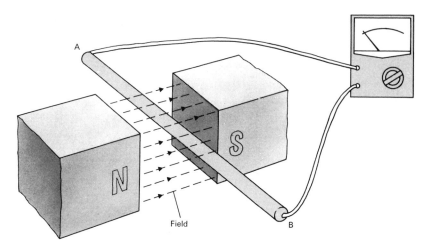

Fig. 3.26   Electromagnetic generation by a conductor 'cutting' through a magnetic field

The above can be explained on the basis that a voltage is generated only when a conductor *cuts* through the magnetic flux. When it moves along them horizontally no flux is 'cut' and hence no voltage is generated.

The idea of a change of linkages in the case of the coil, and the conductor cutting the magnetic field are consistent with each other. It can be seen from Fig. 3.25 that to make more linkages requires the electric circuit to 'cut' through the magnetic field linkages, and similarly if the number of linkages are to be reduced. A basic law of electromagnetic generation can therefore be stated:

To generate a voltage it is essential to have relative motion between a magnetic field and a part of an electric circuit in such a way that either the field is 'cut' or the magnetic flux linkages changed.

Experimental evidence from the above simple experiments also suggests as far as the magnitude of the voltage is concerned:

The greater the rate at which the flux is 'cut' or the magnetic linkages changed, the greater will be the generated voltage. The magnitude of the generated voltage is proportional to the rate of change of the flux linkages.

The direction of the generated voltage depends upon:

(a)   the direction of the magnetic field flux,

(b)   the direction in which the conductor moves relative to the field.

It can be determined by using one of two methods as follows:

(i) *Lenz's law*, which states that the direction of a generated voltage is such that it tends to set up a flow of current, which in turn causes a force opposing the motion which is generating the generated voltage [see Fig. 3.27(a)];

(ii) *Fleming's right-hand rule*, which states that if

> the thuMb points in the direction of Motion
> and the First finger in the direction of the Field
> then the seCond finger gives its direction of Current

[see Fig. 3.27(b)].

Applying these rules to Fig. 3.26 shows that the generated current will flow out of end A if the conductor AB is moved upwards. Thus A becomes the positive terminal and B the negative terminal of the 'generator' insofar as the external circuit is concerned.

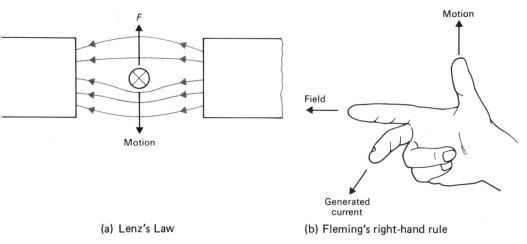

(a) Lenz's Law   (b) Fleming's right-hand rule

Fig. 3.27   Determining the direction of the generated voltage

EQUATION FOR THE GENERATED VOLTAGE

Fig. 3.28 shows another view of Fig. 3.26.

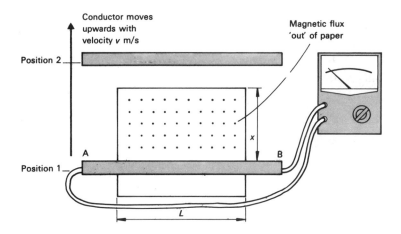

Fig. 3.28   The equation $E = BLv$

Using the basic equation

Generated voltage ∝ Rate of change of flux linkage

we can determine a simple expression for the generated voltage. If AB is moved from position 1 to position 2 at a constant velocity v, then the change of flux linkage with the 'coil' for which AB, the meter and connecting leads form a part, will be the total flux contained in the rectangle shown.

This flux will be

$$\Phi = B \times \text{Area of rectangle}$$

$$\Phi = B \times Lx$$

or $\qquad\qquad \Phi = BLx$

If the time taken to go from position 1 to position 2 is t seconds, then the *rate of change of flux* which is proportional to the generated e is given by

$$e \propto \frac{\Phi}{t} = \frac{BLx}{t}$$

but $\dfrac{x}{t}$ is the velocity v, so $e \propto BLv$.

By a suitable choice of units we can write

$$e = BLv \qquad\qquad\qquad [3.3]$$

where $\quad e =$ generated voltage in volts

$\qquad B =$ magnetic flux density in tesla

$\qquad L =$ length (m) of conductor in magnetic field

$\qquad v =$ velocity (m/s) of conductor perpendicular to the magnetic field

Now consider a conductor in the form of a single turn rectangular coil rotating so that only two sides actually cut flux lines (Figs. 3.29 and 3.30).

Only AB and DC cut flux lines, because BC and DA are in the plane of the flux. The velocity v of AB and CD may be resolved into two components and only $v \sin \theta$ causes flux lines to be cut.

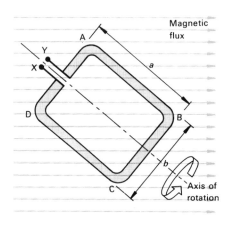

Fig. 3.29   Three-dimensional view of rotating coil

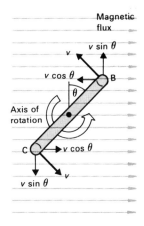

Fig. 3.30   Side view of coil

Applying [3.3], one obtains the voltage e across XY:

$$e = B(\text{AB} + \text{CD})v \sin \theta = 2Bav \sin \theta$$

For circular motion we use $v = r\omega$ (equation [9.12]) and $\omega = \theta/t$

Then $\qquad\qquad\qquad\qquad v = (b/2)\omega$

and $\qquad\qquad\qquad\qquad e = B.ab.\omega.\sin \omega t$

ab is just the area A of the coil. For a coil of n turns, the area nab, which equals nA.

Hence the generated voltage is

$$e = BAn\omega \sin \omega t. \qquad\qquad [3.4]$$

Notice that the output varies with time. The variation is shown in Fig. 3.31.

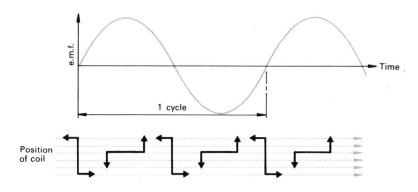

Fig. 3.31   Output voltage (e,m.f.) from a rotating coil

The maximum output occurs when AB and CD are cutting most flux lines per second i.e. when the coil is horizontal.

WORKED EXAMPLE 4

A coil of 250 turns and area 0.2 m² rotates at an angular speed of 60 radians per second in a field of flux density 0.02 T. Calculate the maximum generated voltage.

SOLUTION

Using equation [3.4]

$$e = BAn\omega \sin \omega t$$

Maximum voltage occurs when $\sin \omega t = 1$, i.e. $\omega t = 90°$.

Then
$$e = BAn\omega$$
$$= 0.02 \times 0.2 \times 250 \times 60$$
$$= 60 \text{ V}$$

MUTUAL INDUCTION

We have seen that current in a coil will produce magnetic flux. If we have an iron-cored toroid, as in Fig. 3.32, then there will be magnetic flux as shown.

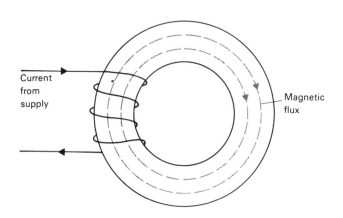

Current from supply

Magnetic flux

Fig. 3.32   Flux in a toroid

If now a second coil is wound on the toroid and the coils are connected as shown in Fig. 3.33, then the following can be observed:

(a) At the moment when switch S is closed, the meter will deflect momentarily showing that a voltage is generated across the second coil.

(b) While S is closed, despite the fact that current flows in coil 1 and, therefore, magnetic flux exists in the ring, there is no voltage across coil 2.

(c) When the switch S is opened, there is again a momentarily deflection of the meter. This time in the opposite direction from that when the switch was closed.

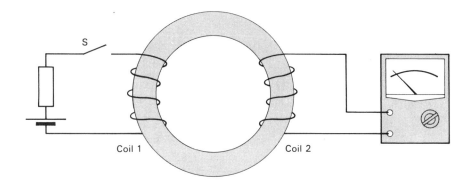

Fig. 3.33   An experiment to show mutual induction

The phenomenon observed is known as *mutual induction*. Although there is no electrical contact between the two coils, it is possible through the medium of the magnetic flux to generate or induce a voltage in the second coil. It will be noted that:

(a) Voltage is only generated if the flux changes. When the flux is constant (constant current in coil 1) there is no voltage across coil 2.

(b) When the flux in coil 2 increases from zero to a certain value as occurs when the switch is closed, the generated voltage is of a certain polarity or direction. When the flux decreases, as occurs on switching off, the generated voltage is of the opposite polarity.

The crucial factor with regard to the generated voltage is the *flux linkage* with coil 2. The flux linkage is the product of the number of turns N_2 in coil 2 and the flux Φ_2 through it. Thus

$$\text{Flux linkages} = N_2 \Phi_2$$

MAGNITUDE OF GENERATED VOLTAGE

The generated voltage is proportional to the *rate of change* of flux-linkages, and if correct units are chosen we can write

Generated voltage in coil 2, e_2 = Rate of change of $(N_2 \Phi_2)$

$$= N_2 \times \text{Rate of change of } \Phi_2$$
(since N_2 is constant)

In calculus notation, this becomes

$$e_2 = \frac{d}{dt}(N_2\Phi_2)$$

or, since N_2 is constant,

$$e_2 = N_2\frac{d\Phi_2}{dt}$$

If N_2 is made very large — that is, we have a large number of turns on coil 2 — the generated voltage can be very great. In fact, much greater than the battery voltage connected across coil 1. This principle is made use of in the motor car ignition system which produces a high voltage across the sparking plug (of the order of several thousand volts) from a 12 V battery. Because the voltage is very high the current is very small. The system is shown in Fig. 3.34.

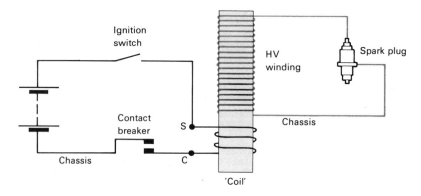

Fig. 3.34   The principle of an ignition system in a motor car

WORKED EXAMPLE 5

The magnetic flux linking a coil of 500 T increases linearly from 10×10^{-4} Wb to 50×10^{-4} Wb over a time interval of 100 ms. Calculate the generated voltage across the terminals of the coil during this time interval.

SOLUTION

We use the equation $e = N\dfrac{d\Phi}{dt}$.

Step 1

Find $\dfrac{d\Phi}{dt}$.

$$\frac{d\Phi}{dt} = \frac{\text{Change of flux}}{\text{Time taken for that change}}$$

$$= \frac{(50-10)\times 10^{-4}\,\text{Wb}}{100\times 10^{-3}\,\text{s}}$$

$$= \frac{40\times 10^{-4}\,\text{Wb}}{10^{-1}\,\text{s}} = 40\times 10^{-3}\,\text{Wb/s}$$

Step 2

$$e = N\times\frac{d\Phi}{dt}$$

$$= 500\times 40\times 10^{-3}\,\text{V}$$

$$= 20\,\text{V}$$

THE TRANSFORMER _____

The transformer is a device for use in a.c. systems. Its operation depends on mutual induction as described in the previous sections. In principle it consists of two separate coils wound on a common iron core, such as shown in Fig. 3.35.

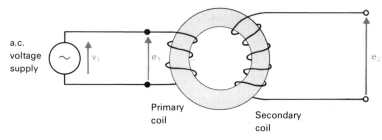

Fig. 3.35   The principle of the transformer

One coil, known as the *primary* coil is connected to an a.c. supply, the other coil, known as the *secondary* coil can feed power to a load or consumer. If the secondary voltage is larger than the primary voltage it is known as a *step-up* transformer. If the secondary voltage is less than the primary, then it is called a *step-down* transformer.

TRANSFORMER ACTION

The voltage applied to the primary coil is sine-wave a.c., and hence the current in the primary coil will be sinusoidal. This will give rise to a sinusoidal flux which will link with the secondary coil. Thus the flux is *continually* changing according to a sine wave pattern and this will generate a voltage across the secondary.

We have

$$e_2 = N_2 \times \text{Rate of change of } \Phi$$

or $$e_2 = N_2 \times \text{Rate of change of sine-wave flux}$$

Now since the rate of change (or differential) of a sine wave is a cosine wave, then the voltage e_2 will be of a cosine form which is, of course, identical in shape to a sine wave. This is one of the reasons for using sine wave supplies, so that the waveform is not changed or distorted in 'passing through' a transformer. The standard symbol for a transformer is shown in Fig. 3.36.

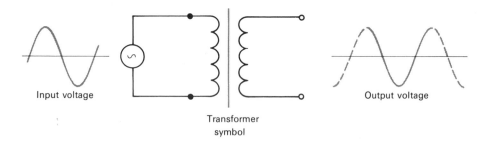

Input voltage   Output voltage

Transformer
symbol

Fig. 3.36   The symbol of a transformer and its input and output waveforms

VOLTAGE RATIO

For the secondary coil, we have

$$e_2 = N_2 \times \text{Rate of } \Phi \qquad [3.5]$$

For the primary coil, since the same flux Φ links with N_1 as well, we have

$$e_1 = N_1 \times \text{Rate of change of } \Phi$$

but $e_1 = v_1$, since there is no voltage drop in the leads connecting them.

Hence $$v_1 = N_1 \times \text{Rate of change of } \Phi \qquad [3.6]$$

Dividing equation [3.6] by [3.5], we have

$$\frac{e_2}{v_1} = \frac{N_2}{N_1}$$

or $$\frac{\text{Secondary voltage}}{\text{Primary voltage}} = \frac{N_2}{N_1}$$ [3.7]

so the ratio of the secondary to primary voltage is the same as the 'turns-ratio' of the transformer.

WORKED EXAMPLE 6

For the safe use of power tools a step-down transformer is required to change the mains voltage of 240 V to 24 V. What turns-ratio is required?

SOLUTION

From equation [3.6] we have

$$\frac{N_2}{N_1} = \frac{\text{Secondary voltage}}{\text{Primary voltage}} = \frac{24}{240} = \frac{1}{10}$$

Therefore the secondary winding should have one-tenth of the number of turns on the primary.

WORKED EXAMPLE 7

Two transformers are linked together as shown in Fig. 3.37. It is required that the output voltage of the second transformer should be 400 V. Calculate the number of secondary turns required for the second transformer.

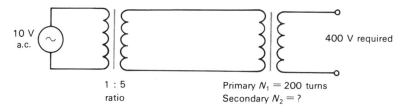

Fig. 3.37   Information for Worked Example 7

SOLUTION

The voltage output of the first transformer will be $10 \times 5 = 50$ V.

For the second transformer we then have, from equation [3.6],

$$\frac{N_2}{N_1} = \frac{400}{50} = \frac{8}{1}$$

and $$N_2 = 8 \times N_1 = 8 \times 200 = 1600 \text{ turns}$$

VOLTAGE AND CURRENT RATIOS

Well-designed transformers are highly efficient, their efficiency can easily exceed 95%. In other words, very little power is lost *in* the transformer itself. Let us assume there are no losses. Then

Power output = Power input

For the transformer shown in Fig. 3.38, if the load is resistive, we have

Power input = $V_1 I_1$ watts

Power output = Power in load = $V_2 I_2$ watts

(the quantities V and I will be in r.m.s. values − see Chapter 4).

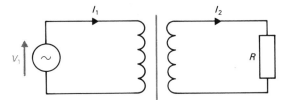

Fig. 3.38   Voltage and current ratios

Therefore if   Power output = Power input

$$V_2 I_2 = V_1 I_1$$

or
$$\frac{V_2}{V_1} = \frac{I_1}{I_2}$$ [3.8]

This means that if we step-up the *voltage* we step-down the *current* and vice versa.

WORKED EXAMPLE 8

A transformer supplies 400 W to a resistance load connected to its secondary. Assuming there are no losses in the transformer and that its turns ratio is 1:2, calculate the primary and secondary currents if the primary voltage is 50 V.

SOLUTION

Since there are no losses

Input power = Output power = 400 W

Therefore $V_1 I_1$ = 400 W   (from equation [3.7])

or $I_1 = \dfrac{400\,\text{W}}{50\,\text{V}} = 8\,\text{A}$

Since the step-up turns ratio is 1:2, the voltage output will be increased two-fold and the current decreased by a half.

Therefore $\qquad$ Output current $= 4\,A$

This can be checked:

$$\text{Output voltage} = 2 \times 50\,V = 100\,V$$

So since $\qquad\qquad\qquad V_2 I_2 = 400\,W$

$$I_2 = \frac{400\,W}{100\,V} = 4\,A$$

EXERCISE 3 _____

Multi-choice questions

1) The basic operation of a moving-coil meter is due to:

   a electromagnetic induction $\qquad$ b interaction of magnetic fields

   c attraction of permanent magnets $\qquad$ d the product of BLv

2) A d.c. motor will work only if it has:

   a windings made from copper wire

   b an electromagnet on the stator

   c a commutator to connect to the windings

   d a reversible d.c. supply

3) The primary and secondary coils of a transformer:

   a always have an electrical connection between them

   b usually give rise to a large power loss

   c always have equal number of turns

   d always have a common magnetic circuit

4) For a step-up transformer:

   a the secondary voltage will be less than the primary voltage

   b the secondary current will be greater than the primary current

   c the secondary power will exceed the primary power

   d the secondary turns will exceed the primary turns

Problems

5)   Draw the magnetic field patterns for the pairs of conductors shown in Fig. 3.39(a) and (b). In each case draw: (a) the individual fields, and (b) the composite or resultant field. Note that ⊗ indicates current into the paper, and ⊙ current out of the paper.

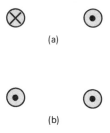

(a)

(b)

Fig. 3.39

6)   For each pair of conductors shown in Fig. 3.39 determine the direction of forces acting on the conductors.

7)   Fleming's left-hand rule refers to three quantities. What are they?

8)   Fig. 3.40 shows a current carrying conductor in a magnetic field. Explain the use of *two* methods to find the direction of the force on the conductor.

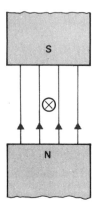

Fig. 3.40

9)   A magnetic flux of $50 \,\mu$Wb exists in an air gap formed by magnetic poles of face size 2 cm × 1 cm. Calculate the flux density in the gap.

10)   The magnet arrangement of a loud speaker is shown in Fig. 3.41. Assume that the mean circumference of the air gap is 4 cm and the depth of the gap 1 cm. If the flux density is 0.1 T, calculate the total flux in the gap.

11) If a single turn coil is placed in the gap of Fig. 3.41 and the current in the coil is 2 A, calculate the force acting on the coil. If when viewed from above the current is clockwise, determine the direction of the force.

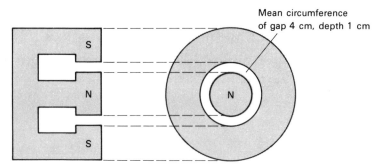

Mean circumference
of gap 4 cm, depth 1 cm

Fig. 3.41

12) A conductor moves at right angles to a magnetic field of flux density 0.2 T. If the effective length of the conductor in the field is 4 cm and it moves with a constant velocity of 100 m/s, calculate the generated voltage.

13) Fig. 3.42 shows two coils wound on iron limbs.

(a) If current is passed through coil 1 only, flowing from the external supply into terminal A, what will be the direction of the magnetic field in the gap?

(b) In what direction should current be passed through coil 2 in order to reduce the flux produced by coil 1?

(c) Show how you would connect both coils in series so that the flux in the gap is greater than in case (a), assuming that the current will be the same value as in (a).

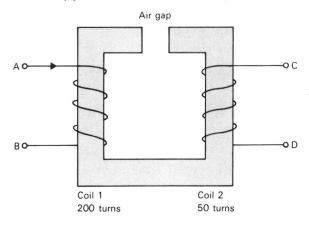

Air gap

A ○ →

B ○

○ C

○ D

Coil 1
200 turns

Coil 2
50 turns

Fig. 3.42

14) The magnetic flux linking a coil varies as shown in the graph of flux versus time in Fig. 3.43. State:

(a) over which interval(s) of time will a voltage be generated in the coil;

(b) over which interval(s) of time will the polarity of the generated voltage be the same;

(c) over which interval(s) of time will the polarity of the generated voltage be opposite to that of (b).

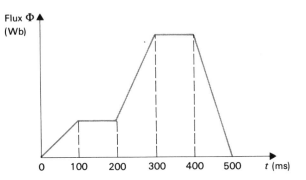

Fig. 3.43

15) If the flux linking a coil varies as shown in Fig. 3.44, state at what times the generated voltage in the coil will be zero.

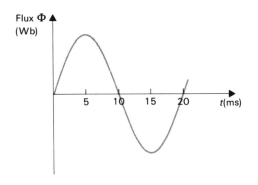

Fig. 3.44

16) The flux linking a coil increases linearly at the rate of 0.2 Wb/s. If the generated voltage is 30 V, calculate the number of turns of the coil.

17) When 24 V a.c. is applied to the primary of Transformer A the secondary voltage is 120 V. Transformer B supplies power to a load. The load current is 1 A when the primary current is 0.5 A.

(a) Determine the turns ratio of each transformer.

(b) Show how you would use both transformers to obtain a voltage of 60 V from a 24 V a.c. supply.

(c) What is the smallest voltage output that could be obtained from a 24 V a.c. supply using both transformers?

18) In Table 3.1, column 1 shows some well-known equations that represent quantities given in column 2. Units of these quantities are shown in column 3. Arrange the quantities given in columns 2 and 3 so that they correspond with the equation in column 1. (Quantities can be used more than once.)

TABLE 3.1

Column 1	Column 2	Column 3
Equation	Represents	Units
BLI	Flux density	Weber
$\dfrac{V_2}{V_1}$	Generated voltage	Newton
BA	Force on a conductor	Volt
$N\dfrac{d\Phi}{dt}$	Turns ratio	Tesla
$\dfrac{\Phi}{A}$	Transformer primary power	Watt
BLv	Magnetic flux	None
$V_1 I_1$		

19) Two metal rails A and B are inclined so that a circular metal rod can roll down them as in Fig. 3.45. An ammeter is connected across the ends of the rails. If there is a magnetic flux vertically downwards between the rails, produced by a permanent magnet (not shown):

(a) Describe what happens when the rod rolls down the rails with reference to: (i) generated voltage and current, (ii) electromagnetic force acting on the rod.

(b) Determine the direction of the current in the ammeter.

(c) Determine the direction of force on the rod C due to current in the circuit. (Assume that the rod rolls at constant velocity.)

Magnetic flux

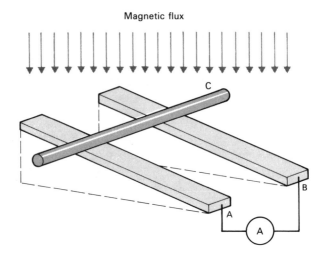

Fig. 3.45

20) A coil of 200 turns, with a coil side of active length 300 mm rotates in a uniform magnetic field of 0.3 T. If the conductor speed is 5 m/s, calculate: (a) the maximum e.m.f. generated in the coil, (b) the e.m.f. generated at the instant when the conductors are 30° from the maximum position.

ALTERNATING CURRENTS

After reaching the end of this chapter you should be able to:

1. *State possible sources of sine wave voltage.*
2. *Define instantaneous, peak and r.m.s. values of a sine wave and calculate them from given data.*
3. *Show that r.m.s. value is $1/\sqrt{2}$ of peak value by considering power dissipation in a resistor.*
4. *Define frequency, cycle, and periodic time and state the relationship between them.*
5. *Calculate a.c. voltage and current values in simple resistive circuits and sketch the waveforms.*
6. *Calculate power in simple a.c. resistive circuits.*
7. *Describe the action of simple single-phase and three-phase alternators.*
8. *Define phase and line voltages and state the relationship between them.*

ALTERNATING VOLTAGE AND CURRENT

The electricity mains supply for domestic and industrial use is an *alternating voltage.* When a circuit, such as an electric fire, is connected to the supply an alternating current will flow through the fire element. Although the abbreviation a.c. strictly stands for alternating current, the abbreviation a.c. is widely used as an adjective to signify an alternating supply or quantity be it voltage or current. Thus phrases such as a.c. voltage, a.c. current and a.c. supply are commonplace.

The *waveform* of the a.c. supply has a special shape. It is a sine wave. This means that a graph of voltage or current against time will have a sine wave or sinusoidal shape. The waveform of the mains supply can be observed on a cathode ray oscilloscope (CRO) and a typical display is shown in Fig. 4.1.

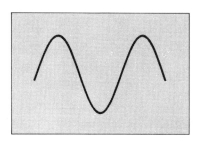

Fig. 4.1   The a.c. mains waveform

A method of displaying the a.c. mains waveform on a CRO is shown in Fig. 4.2. For safety a transformer with an output voltage of 2–10 V is connected between the a.c. mains supply and the CRO. (*Warning*: Do not attempt to do this with the mains supply without supervision as it could be dangerous.)

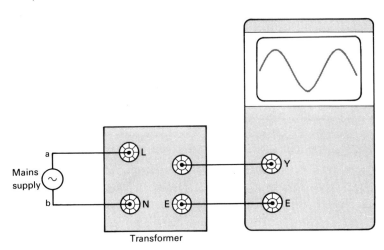

Fig. 4.2   A circuit for displaying a.c. on a CRO

The waveform of Fig. 4.3 shows the variation of the voltage V_{ab} (Y–axis) with time (X-axis). The time-scale is in milliseconds (ms). It is seen that:

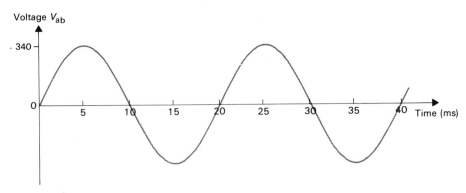

Fig. 4.3   An a.c. voltage waveform

(a)   The voltage V_{ab} is sometimes positive (as between 0 and 10 ms) and sometimes negative (as between 10 ms and 20 ms).

(b)   The positive and negative parts are identical in shape except that one is 'upside down'. These are called *half-cycles*.

(c) The pattern repeats itself every 20 ms, that is, it is the same between 20 ms and 40 ms as it is from 0 to 20 ms. This pattern is called a *cycle*. Since each cycle occupies 20 ms there will be 50 cycles in one second.

(d) When the waveform is positive, V_{ab} is positive which means that during that time terminal a is positive with respect to terminal b. When the waveform is negative it means that terminal a is negative with respect to terminal b.

(e) The waveform follows a smooth sine wave pattern increasing from 0 to a maximum value of 340 V (despite the fact that the mains voltage is labelled 240 V – the reason for this will be explained later) and decreases again to 0. The pattern is then repeated in the negative direction. The value of the voltage at any time could be found from the equation

$$V_{ab} = 340 \sin \theta$$

the value of θ would have to be worked out proportionally by noting that 20 ms corresponds to 360°.

SOME DEFINITIONS

Fig. 4.4 shows one cycle of a sine wave labelled with the terms usually used.

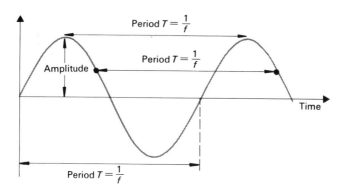

Fig. 4.4 Sine-wave definitions

Waveform. This is the shape of the voltage/time or current/time wave. For a.c. circuits it is always sinusoidal.

Amplitude or Peak Value (V_{max} or I_{max}). This is the maximum value of the alternating quantity. It can be taken on the maximum positive or negative value.

Cycle. This is the basic pattern which repeats itself.

Period or Periodic Time (*T*). This is the time for one cycle. It can be measured as the time between two identical points on consecutive cycles (see Fig. 4.4).

Frequency (*f*). This is the number of cycles in one second. For the UK mains supply the frequency is 50 cycles per second or 50 Hz. (Hz is the abbreviation for Hertz which is the name given to one cycle per second.)

Instantaneous value (*v or i*). This is the value of the quantity at any instant of time.

RELATIONSHIP BETWEEN FREQUENCY AND PERIODIC TIME

The frequency is the number of cycles or complete 'patterns' that will fit into one second. Since each cycle occupies *T* seconds, then:

$$f = \frac{1\,(\text{cycle})}{T\,(\text{seconds})} \text{ cycles per second or Hz}$$

so to find frequency from periodic time we use

$$f = \frac{1}{T} \qquad\qquad [4.1]$$

or to find the periodic time given the frequency, we use

$$T = \frac{1}{f} \qquad\qquad [4.2]$$

WORKED EXAMPLE 1

For the waveform of Fig. 4.5 determine the voltage v_{ab} when *t* is: (a) 9 ms, (b) 18 ms, (c) 27 ms, (d) 39 ms.

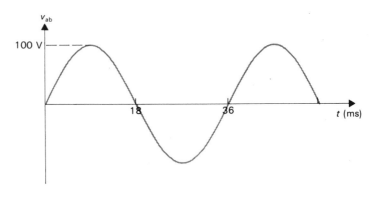

Fig. 4.5   Information for Worked Example

SOLUTION

(a)   When $t = 9\,\text{ms}$, v_{ab} will be at its maximum peak value, i.e. $v_{ab} = +100\,\text{V}$.

(b)   When $t = 18\,\text{ms}$, the voltage is zero at that instant.

(c)   When $t = 27\,\text{ms}$, v_{ab} will be on maximum – the negative direction and since the waveform is symmetrical the $v_{ab} = -100\,\text{V}$.

(d)   When $t = 39\,\text{ms}$, v_{ab} will be the same value as when 3 ms. Recognising that 36 ms corresponds to 360°, we see that 3 ms corresponds to 30° position.

The equation of v_{ab} will be

$$v_{ab} = 100 \sin \theta$$

so at $t = 3\,\text{ms}$
$$v_{ab} = 100 \sin 30°$$
$$= 100 \times \tfrac{1}{2}$$

or
$$v_{ab} = 50\,\text{V at that instant}$$

WORKED EXAMPLE 2

(a)   Calculate the periodic time of sine waveforms of frequencies (i) 50 Hz, (ii) 1 MHz.

(b)   Calculate the frequencies of waveforms having periodic times of (i) 25 ms, (ii) 1 ms, (iii) 20 ns.

SOLUTION

(a)   Using $T = \dfrac{1}{f}$ (equation [4.2]), we have

(i) $T = \dfrac{1}{50}\text{s}$ or $\dfrac{1000}{50}\text{ms} = 20\,\text{ms}$

(ii) $T = \dfrac{1}{1 \times 10^6}\text{s} = 10^{-6}\text{s} = 1\,\mu\text{s}$

(b)   Using $f = \dfrac{1}{T}$ (equation [4.1]), we have

(i) $f = \dfrac{1}{25 \times 10^{-3}\text{s}} = \dfrac{10^3}{25} = 40\,\text{Hz}$

(ii) $f = \dfrac{1}{1 \times 10^{-3}\text{s}} = \dfrac{10^3}{1} = 1000\,\text{Hz}$ or   1 kHz

(iii) $f = \dfrac{1}{20 \times 10^{-9}\text{s}} = \dfrac{10^9}{20} = 50 \times 10^6\,\text{Hz}$ or   50 MHz

SINE-WAVE GENERATORS

The turbine-driven a.c. generators at power stations are known as *alternators.* They are designed to produce a sinusoidal voltage waveform. It will be recalled that to generate a voltage, relative motion between an electrical conductor and a magnetic field is required. In alternators it is the magnetic field that moves while the conductors in which the voltage appears are stationary. The magnetic field is, therefore, produced by the rotor (the rotating part) whilst the conductors or windings are on the stator (the stationary part). A cross-section of an alternator is shown in Fig. 4.6(a).

The conductor AA′ is shown as one turn [Fig. 4.6(b)]. It could, however, be a coil of several turns with two ends A and A′.

The shape or profile of the rotor is designed so that the magnetic flux distribution around the air gap is sinusoidal. Thus, when the rotor rotates at a constant speed, the generated voltage in the stator conductors will be sinusoidal as shown in Fig. 4.6(c).

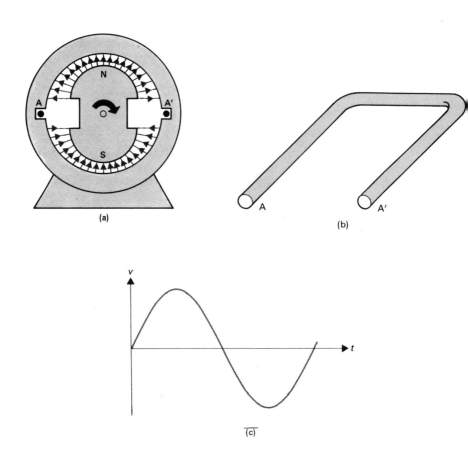

Fig. 4.6   A salient pole alternator: (a) its cross-section, (b) one turn of its conductor, (c) the sinusoidal waveform generated by it

The sequence of events producing the sinusoidal voltage is shown in Fig. 4.7. It should be remembered that the rotor is always rotating at a constant speed. As it moves through position 1 there is no change of magnetic flux cutting or linking the conductors, so the generated voltage is zero. In position 2 the rate of magnetic flux 'cutting' the conductor is a maximum and so the voltage will be a maximum. When the rotor moves through position 3 the voltage is again zero. In position 4 the voltage again reaches a maximum but this time in an opposite direction, and in position 5 the cycle of events is again repeated.

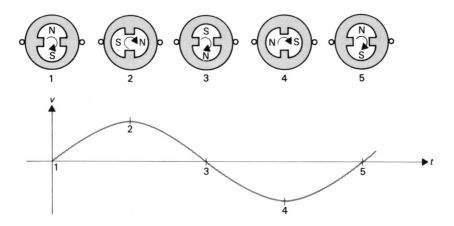

Fig. 4.7   The generation of a sine wave voltage

Thus every complete rotation of the rotor corresponds to one cycle of generated voltage. Since the mains frequency is 50 cycles per second or 50×60, i.e. 3000 cycles per minute, it means that the two-pole rotor alternator we have described should be rotated at 3000 r.p.m.

Large alternators do not have a permanent magnet rotor as described above. Instead windings on the rotor are fed, via slip rings, with direct-current (d.c.) to produce a high-intensity magnetic field.

SINGLE-PHASE AND THREE-PHASE SUPPLIES

The system described above is known as a *single-phase* alternator. In practice, all large alternators generate *three-phase* voltages. A three-phase alternator can be thought of as three single-phase alternators in one. The principle is shown in Fig. 4.8.

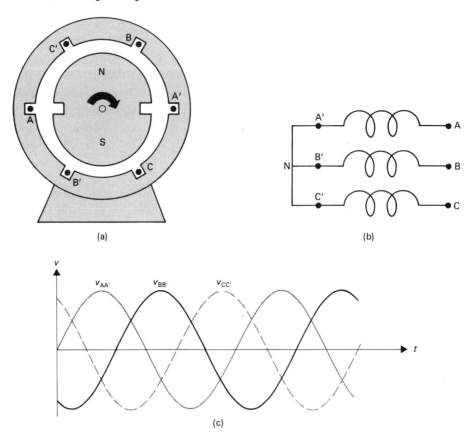

Fig. 4.8   A simple two-pole, three-phase alternator: (a) its cross-section, (b) how its conductors are connected, (c) the waveforms generated from it

In addition to one winding AA′ in the single-phase generator we now have a further two windings BB′ and CC′. These are spread evenly around the stator and it will be noted that corresponding ends A, B and C are 120° apart. One end of each winding A′B′C′ is connected together to form the 'neutral' point N.

When the rotor rotates, voltages will be generated in each winding, but the waveforms will be out of 'step' or, put another way, *not in phase* with each other.

As far as coil AA′ is concerned the waveform will be as described previously in Fig. 4.6. The voltage in coil BB′ will reach a maximum when the rotor has turned through 120° and the waveform will, therefore, be 120° out of phase with that of coil AA′. Similarly the voltage in coil CC′ will be 120° out of phase with that of BB′.

The voltage waveforms in Fig. 4.8(c) could be labelled AN, BN, and CN because points A′, B′ and C′ are the same as N. To distribute three-phase power requires only four wires or conductors, A, B, C and N. In fact, sometimes the neutral or N conductor can be dispensed with. This is, therefore, much more economical than having six conductors, that is, two from each of three separate generators. The arrangement also makes much more effective use of the magnetic material and circuit of a generator.

In a three-phase system such as we have described there will be two sets of voltages:

(a) 'phase' voltages which exist between 'live' and the neutral point, V_{AN}, V_{BN} and V_{CN}. These will all be of the same magnitude.

(b) 'line' voltage V_{AB}, V_{BC} and V_{CA}. Each of these will again be of the same magnitude.

However, the 'line' voltages will be larger than the 'phase' voltages, in fact, $\sqrt{3}$ times as great. Thus a three-phase system can provide us with two voltages. The domestic supply for our homes is a single-phase supply of 240 V[†] but is obtained from a three-phase system having a line voltage of 415 V.

DISTRIBUTION OF ELECTRICAL ENERGY. _____

The electrical power is taken from power stations by transmission lines consisting of overhead cables (Fig. 4.9). These usually consist of two sets of three cables. This system, known as the National Grid System is a network of cables stretching throughout the country and linking all power stations. By means of the grid, power can be distributed to wherever the demand is and also ensures reliability of the supply should any power station break down.

A diagram of a typical distribution system is shown in Fig. 4.10 (pp 120–1). Large modern power stations generate electricity at 25 000 V. This is 'stepped up' by transformers to 275 000 V or 400 000 V for connection to the Grid System. It may then be 'stepped down' to 132 000 V for smaller grid systems and further reduced to 33 000 V and 11 000 V for local distribution. Thereafter these voltage are reduced to 415 V three-phase distribution and 240 V single-phase.

[†] This is the r.m.s. value. For the meaning of r.m.s. see p. 126.

Fig. 4.9   The Sizewall-Sundon 400 000 V transmission line

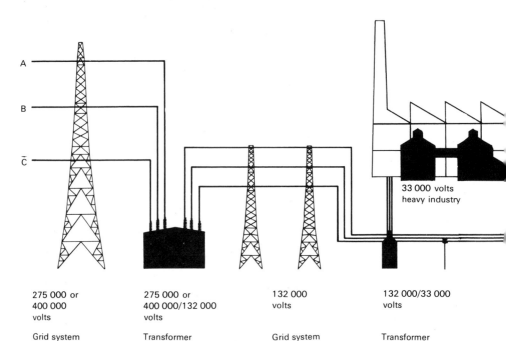

275 000 or 400 000 volts	275 000 or 400 000/132 000 volts	132 000 volts	132 000/33 000 volts
Grid system	Transformer	Grid system	Transformer

33 000 volts
heavy industry

Long distance transmission is at the highest voltage possible as this keeps the current low, which means that 'thinner' cables can be used. Most of the distribution system is on three-phase. Single-phase distribution is used only locally, mainly for domestic purposes.

AC CIRCUITS

An a.c. circuit is one which contains an a.c. supply. This can be the a.c. mains supply which will always be 50 Hz or a signal generator which can produce waveforms of other frequencies. In all cases the waveform will be sinusoidal. Whilst we can connect several components such as resistors, capacitors, inductors and transformers to a.c. generators, in this case we will consider circuits that have only resistors.

A basic circuit is shown in Fig. 4.11.

A resistor R is connected to the terminals a and b of an a.c. generator of voltage v. (A small v denotes the instantaneous voltage at any time and a small i the corresponding instantaneous current.) The + and − signs alongside the generator symbol should not be confused with d.c. They are used

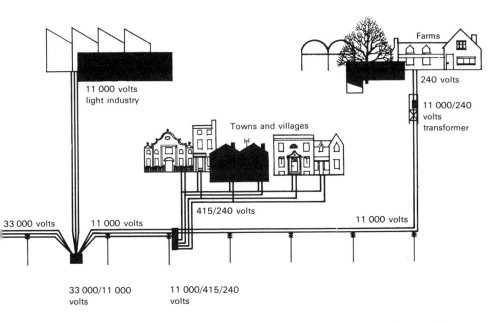

Fig. 4.10   The electricity distribution system

here to indicate a reference direction, so that when we say that v is $+ 5$ V we know that the top terminal is at that instant positive by 5 V with respect to the lower terminal. If we say $v = -2$ V, it means that at that instant the top terminal is negative with respect to the lower terminal.

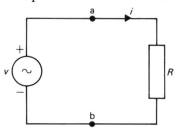

Fig. 4.11   A basic a.c. circuit

The current i is also given a reference direction as shown by the arrow. If $i = +2$A, it flows in the direction shown at that instant. If $i = -3$A, it means that at that instant of time the current is in the opposite direction to that indicated.

The relationship at any instant between the voltage across R, v_{ab}, and the current through it is given by

$$\frac{v_{ab}}{i} = R$$

or, since v_{ab} is the same as v, we have

$$\frac{v}{i} = R \qquad [4.3]$$

or

$$v = iR \qquad [4.4]$$

Since R is a constant, this last equation means that v and i will always have the same waveform or shape, and that they will be in step or in phase with each other. It means that both will always be sine waves in step with each other as shown in Fig. 4.12.

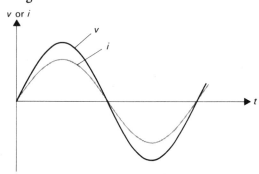

Fig. 4.12   Voltage and current waveforms for the circuit of Fig. 4.11 are in phase

WORKED EXAMPLE 3

A resistor of $10\,\Omega$ is connected to an a.c. supply of peak value $10\,V$. Sketch: (a) one cycle of the voltage, and (b) the current waveforms.

SOLUTION

The circuit is shown in Fig. 4.13(a).

The waveform may be plotted as follows. Since the frequency is not given, we will use a time-scale in terms of T the periodic time. Then remember that the voltage is given at any time by $v = 10 \sin \theta$, we can obtain the values of voltage as shown. The current i is given by v/R (from equation [4.4]) and can, therefore, be calculated for each corresponding value of voltage.

Time	0	$\frac{1}{12}T$	$\frac{2}{12}T$	$\frac{3}{12}T$	$\frac{4}{12}T$	$\frac{5}{12}T$	$\frac{T}{2}$
Corresponding angle	0	$30°$	$60°$	$90°$	$120°$	$150°$	$180°$
Voltage $= 10 \sin \theta$	0	5	8.67	10	8.67	5	0
Current $i = \dfrac{v}{R} = \dfrac{v}{10}$	0	0.5	0.87	1	0.87	0.5	0

The negative half-cycle will have identical values, except that both voltage and current are then negative. The waveforms are shown in Fig. 4.13(b).

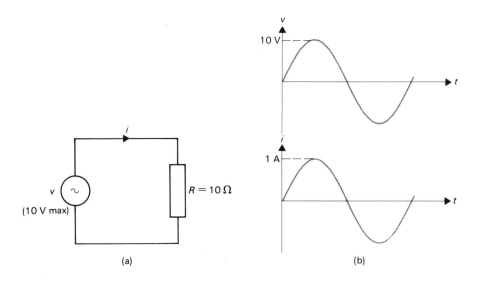

Fig. 4.13   The solution to Worked Example 3

POWER IN AC CIRCUITS

Fig. 4.14(a) shows a resistor (which could be an electric fire) connected to an a.c. supply. The current will be a sine waveform as shown in Fig. 4.14(b).

The power dissipated in the resistor R at any instant of time will be given by

$$\text{Power} = i^2R$$

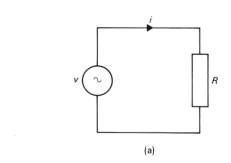

(a)

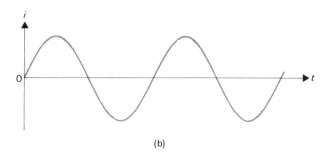

(b)

Fig. 4.14   (a) An a.c. circuit, (b) its current

We can show this graphically as follows. Suppose the current is as shown in Fig. 4.15 (as having a maximum value of 10 A). Suppose R is 10 Ω, then at any instant of time – we will take intervals of 2 ms – we can calculate the power as i^2R by squaring the value of the current at that instant and multiplying by 10, the value of R. For example, when $t = 5$ ms, $i = 10$ A so $P = i^2R = 10^2 \times 10 = 1000$ W. When $t = 11.67$ ms, $i = -5$ A, so $P = (-5)^2 10 = 250$ W.

It will be noted that the power is always positive. That is, the power waveform is always above the base line. Physically this is obvious, because heat will be given out by the resistor no matter in what direction the current flows through it.

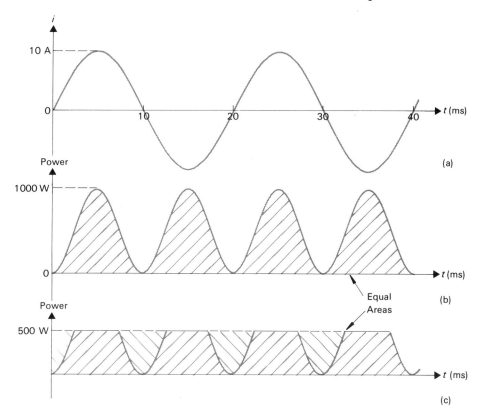

Fig. 4.15   (a) Current and (b) power in an a.c. circuit. (c) shows that the power of 1000 W a.c. is equivalent to a constant (or d.c.) power of 500 W

Now it will be noticed that the power is varying all the time. It reaches a maximum of 1000 W every 10 ms and then decreases to zero. To us the heat coming out of an electric fire appears constant. What we are interested in is the average energy that comes out of the fire over a period of time very much greater than 10 ms.

Since the energy or heat is (power × time), it will be represented by the area under the power/time curve. In this case it is easy to find this area as shown in Fig. 4.15(c).

The peaks will fit into the troughs to give a rectangle of 'height' 500 W. Thus the total heat energy dissipated in R over a period of time will be the same as if the power was constant at 500 W all the time, and not fluctuating as it does.

EFFECTIVE OR RMS VALUE

Suppose we had used a d.c. supply in the previous case, what value of current would we have needed to give the same power dissipation of 500 W? This we can find as follows:

Since $$P = I^2R$$

we have $$500 = I^2 \times 10$$

or $$I^2 = 50$$

so $$I = 7.07\,A$$

Therefore, a *direct current* of 7.07 A will produce the same power as a sine wave a.c. of *peak value* 10 A. This is a very useful way of comparing a.c. and d.c. We compare the *power* they produce. We can, therefore, say that the *effective value* as far as power is concerned of a sine wave a.c. is

$$7.07 \div 10 \quad \text{or} \quad 0.707 \text{ of the peak value of the a.c.}$$

The figure 0.707 is in fact $1/\sqrt{2}$ and is easier remembered in that form. Effective value is also known as 'root mean square' abbreviated to r.m.s. We can refer to the r.m.s. value of an a.c. voltage or current. In either case

$$\text{r.m.s. value} = \frac{\text{Peak value}}{\sqrt{2}}$$

so $$V_{r.m.s.} = \frac{V_{max}}{\sqrt{2}} \qquad [4.5]$$

and $$I_{r.m.s.} = \frac{I_{max}}{\sqrt{2}} \qquad [4.6]$$

Unless otherwise stated, r.m.s. values are always quoted for a.c. voltages and currents. Thus for the 240 V a.c. domestic supply, the 240 V refers to its r.m.s. value. All a.c. meters are calibrated to read r.m.s. values.

The r.m.s. value of an a.c. voltage or current is equal to the value of a d.c. voltage or current which will produce the same amount of power in a given resistor. For sine waves the r.m.s. value is given by $\frac{\text{Peak value}}{\sqrt{2}}$.

WORKED EXAMPLE 4

What is the peak value of the 240 V a.c. mains?

SOLUTION

Since $V_{rms} = \dfrac{V_{max}}{\sqrt{2}}$ (equation [4.5])

we have V_{max} or $V_{peak} = \sqrt{2}V$ r.m.s.

$$= \sqrt{2} \times 240 \text{ V} = 340 \text{ V}$$

WORKED EXAMPLE 5

The maximum height of an a.c. waveform displayed on an oscilloscope is 5 cm. If each cm represents 2 V, what is the r.m.s. value of the voltage?

SOLUTION

$$\text{Peak voltage} = 5 \times 2 = 10 \text{ V}$$

$$\text{r.m.s. voltage} = \frac{10\text{ V}}{\sqrt{2}} = 7.07 \text{ V}$$

SPECIAL PROPERTIES OF SINE WAVES

You may wonder why sine waves have such a special place in electrical engineering. The sine wave is special in two ways:

(a) Any waveform whatever shape it is can be 'broken down' into several sine waves.

(b) If a sine wave voltage is applied to a circuit consisting of resistors, capacitors, inductors and transformers, then the current will always be a sine wave and of the same frequency, although it may not be in step. The same cannot be said of other waveforms such as square waves. Thus a sine wave never loses its identity in a circuit, and we can say 'once a sine wave, always a sine wave'.

EXERCISE 4

Problem

1) Calculate the periodic time of waveforms having the following frequencies: 25 Hz, 1000 Hz, 20 kHz, 5 MHz.

2) Calculate the frequencies of waveforms having the following periodic times: 50 ms, 2 ms, 100 µs, 250 ns.

3) Sketch on the same axes (i.e. superimposed on each other) two cycles of sine waveforms A and B, where

A has an amplitude of 10 V and frequency 50 Hz

B has an amplitude of 4 V and frequency 100 Hz

4) A voltage waveform is shown in Fig. 4.16 with certain quantities A, B etc. Complete the table below with the appropriate letters. Note that more than one letter can be used on one line.

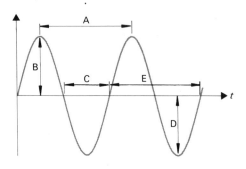

Fig. 4.16

Amplitude	
Frequency	
Periodic time	
Negative peak value	
One-half periodic time	

5) The two waveforms A and B in Fig. 4.17 below are drawn to the same scale. Determine the amplitude and frequency of waveform B.

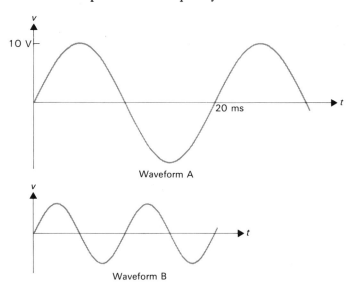

Fig. 4.17

6) Fig. 4.18 shows a voltage waveform displayed on a CRO. If one vertical division represents 5 V and 1 horizontal division is 1 ms, calculate the amplitude and frequency of the waveform.

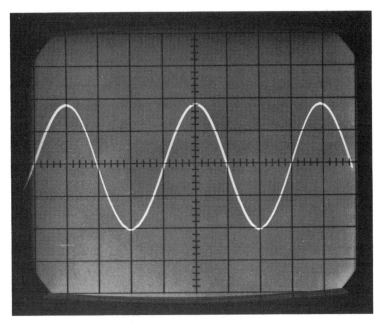

Fig. 4.18

7) A simple two-pole generator of the type in Fig. 4.6 is used to generate a sinusoidal voltage. Calculate the speed of the rotor in rev/min for frequencies of: (a) 50 Hz, (b) 25 Hz, (c) 100 Hz.

8) A resistor of 100 Ω is connected to a 50 Hz a.c. supply of peak value 100 V. Sketch one cycle of the voltage and current waveforms.

9) For the circuit of Fig. 4.19 sketch one cycle of the voltage waveforms V_{AC} and V_{BC}.

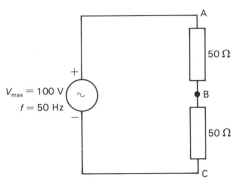

Fig. 4.19

10) For the circuit of Fig. 4.20 calculate: (a) the peak current in the circuit, (b) the peak voltage across the 100 Ω resistor.

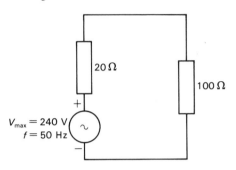

Fig. 4.20

11) The voltage across the 1 Ω resistor in Fig. 4.21(a) is displayed on a CRO. The waveform is shown in Fig. 4.21(b). Determine: (a) the current flowing through the 100 Ω, (b) the voltage of the a.c. source.

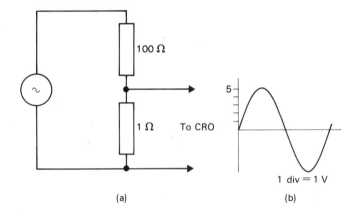

Fig. 4.21

12) Calculate the r.m.s. values of a.c. current waveforms of peak values: 2 A, 5 A, 30 A, 141 A.

13) The power dissipated in a 10 Ω resistor connected to an a.c. supply is 40 W. Calculate the peak value of the current.

14) A resistor of 20 Ω can be connected to either: (a) an a.c. supply of peak value 25 V, (b) a battery of terminal voltage 24 V. In which condition will the power dissipated in the resistor be greatest?

15) A resistor of 200 Ω can be connected to either: (i) a 240 V a.c. mains supply or (ii) a 240 V d.c. supply. Will the power taken from the supply in case (ii) be: (a) greater, (b) equal, (c) less, than in case (i)?

THE CATHODE RAY OSCILLOSCOPE[†]

After reaching the end of this chapter you should be able to:

1. *Describe how a simple CRO is adjusted to give (a) a spot trace, (b) a continuous horizontal trace on the screen, explaining the functions of the various controls.*
2. *Use a CRO to (a) display a sinusoidal signal and measure the amplitude and frequency, (b) measure potential difference.*

SUMMARY

The CRO is an instrument for measuring voltage and time. It displays a waveform on the screen and enables characteristics of the waveform to be observed and measured, and in particular for a sine wave their amplitude and frequency.

The CRO has *three* major sections: (a) the CRT controls, (b) the Y-amplifier, (c) the time-base. The gain of the Y amplifier which controls the height of the trace is adjustable by means of the VOLTS/CM switch. The speed of the time-base which controls the speed the spot moves across the face of the tube can be varied by means of the TIME/CM switch.

Mechanical quantities can be transduced to voltage and observed on the CRO. Double-beam CROs enable two waveforms to be compared.

THE DISPLAY OF A CRO

A typical cathode ray oscilloscope (CRO) is shown in Fig. 5.1. It is a versatile measuring instrument of great value to the engineer. Basically it can measure *time* and *voltage*. Time intervals from a few microseconds (μs) or less up to several seconds and voltages from a few microvolts (μV) up to several hundreds of volts can be measured. Because of its rapid response it can observe and measure events which could not otherwise be seen by the human eye.

---

†   Further information on the CRO may be found in:
     (i) *Physics for TEC Level II* (also from Stanley Thornes)
     (ii) Rees, D.T. *The Cathode Ray Oscilloscope* (Longman, 1978)

Fig. 5.1   A typical CRO

The display is seen on the *screen* of a cathode ray tube (CRT). The display is produced by a spot moving at a constant speed horizontally across the screen, and if it moves very rapidly it appears as a line. The spot may simultaneously be moved vertically on the screen by applying a voltage to the Y or *vertical input terminals.* The vertical movement is proportional to the applied voltage. Hence:

(a)   the X-axis is a linear time scale,

(b)   the Y-axis is a linear voltage scale,

(c)   the display is a graph of voltage against time.

The CRO may be represented as a block diagram as in Fig. 5.2. Normally the voltage applied to the Y-input terminals are amplified by the *y-amplifier* before being applied to the CRT. The spot is moved horizontally by the *time base.* It is moved from left to right at a constant speed and then rapidly returned (too fast to be seen) to the left side and the process repeated.

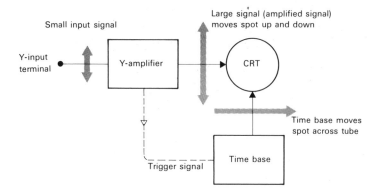

Fig. 5.2   A block diagram for a CRO

The versatility of the CRO for engineering use is based on the fact that many physical quantities may be easily converted into a voltage by means of a *transducer.* Thus the display on the screen can represent variations of speed, torque, temperature etc., with time.

THE CONTROLS OF A CRO

To use a CRO the first thing to do is to adjust the controls to obtain a fine horizontal line across the middle of the screen. To achieve this it is important to realise that there are *three* sets or groups of controls on every CRO. These are as shown in Fig. 5.3 and are:

(a)   Those controls which act directly on the cathode ray tube and influence the 'quality' of the trace — how bright and how fine it is. These are generally called *intensity* (or *brightness*) and *focus.* Frequently the *on–off* switch is incorporated with these controls.

(b)   The vertical or Y-amplifier controls. The *volts/cm* or *sensitivity* switch has several switched positions and controls the gain of the Y-amplifier. It is used to obtain a trace of suitable height on the screen.

The *y-shift* control enables the trace (or spot, or line) to be moved bodily up or down. Here also are two input terminals (Y and E) to which the voltage to be measured is connected.

(c)   The controls of the *time-base* section. These control the horizontal motion of the spot.

The *time/cm* control has several switched positions which change the speed of the spot across the screen. In the *off* position the spot is stationary and may be moved to the centre of the screen by the *x-shift.*

The various *trigger* controls are used to obtain a stationary display of a waveform.

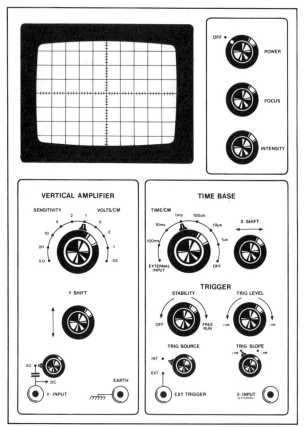

Fig. 5.3   The controls of a typical CRO

In using any CRO always identify these three groupings of the controls and remember that the functions they control are independent of each other. For example, only the vertical amplifier controls will influence the vertical motion of the spot. Using this approach makes it easy to use any CRO.

USING THE CRO

If possible obtain a CRO. Identify all the controls and their function. Fig. 5.4 will help you. Even if your CRO is not identical to the one shown you should still be able to relate it to the chart.

Set the controls as indicated on the chart, noting that:

(a)   the VOLTS/CM switch is set to its least sensitive position, i.e. maximum volts/cm;

Scopex 4S 6

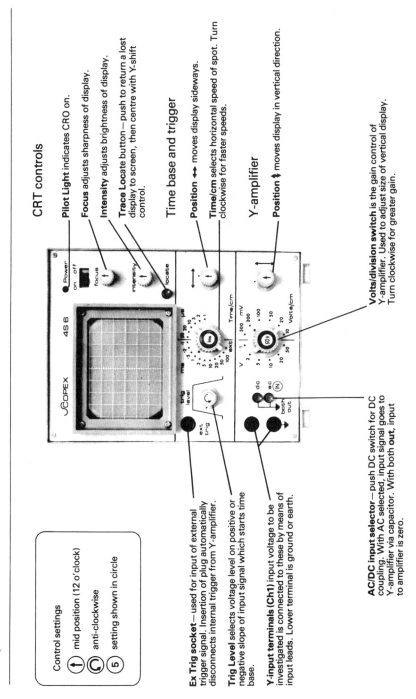

Control settings

⊕ mid position (12 o'clock)

⟲ anti-clockwise

⑤ setting shown in circle

CRT controls

Pilot Light indicates CRO on.

Focus adjusts sharpness of display.

Intensity adjusts brightness of display.

Trace Locate button — push to return a lost display to screen, then centre with Y-shift control.

Time base and trigger

Position ↔ moves display sideways.

Time/cm selects horizontal speed of spot. Turn clockwise for faster speeds.

Y-amplifier

Position ↕ moves display in vertical direction.

Volts/division switch is the gain control of Y-amplifier. Used to adjust size of vertical display. Turn clockwise for greater gain.

Ex Trig socket — used for input of external trigger signal. Insertion of plug automatically disconnects internal trigger from Y-amplifier.

Trig Level selects voltage level on positive or negative slope of input signal which starts time base.

Y-input terminals (Ch1) input voltage to be investigated is connected to these by means of input leads. Lower terminal is ground or earth.

AC/DC input selector — push DC switch for DC coupling. With AC selected, input signal goes to Y-amplifier via capacitor. With both **out**, input to amplifier is zero.

Fig. 5.4 A diagram identifying the controls of a CRO

(b) the TIME/CM switch should be set to 1 ms/cm;

(c) all other controls should be set mid-way except TRIGGER controls.

Plug your CRO into a mains socket and switch on.

After a few minutes you should have a horizontal line on the screen. Use the Y-shift to centre it (and if necessary the X-shift) and obtain a fine focus and reasonable brightness by using the FOCUS and INTENSITY controls. If you have difficulty refer to Fig. 5.5

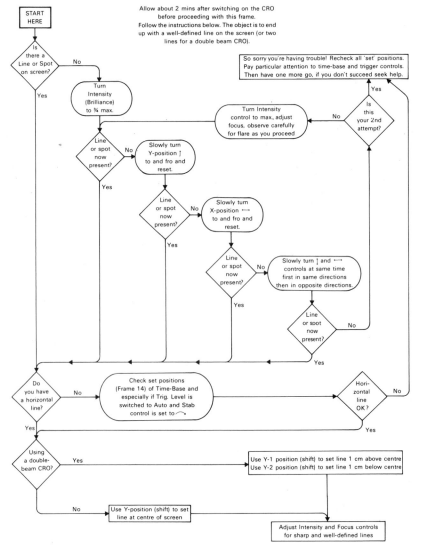

Fig. 5.5   How to get a trace (a line) on a CRO screen

To obtain a spot on the screen, switch off the time-base (TIME/CM switch) and adjust the X-shift to centre the spot. (*Warning*: do not have the spot too bright or it may leave a burn mark on the screen, so turn the intensity down.)

Carry out the following operations on the controls and note the effect:

	Operation	*Effect*
1.	Rotate INTENSITY control to and fro	
2.	Rotate FOCUS control to and fro	
3.	Turn Y-POSITION control anticlockwise	
4.	Turn X-POSITION control anticlockwise	
5.	Adjust controls to place spot at X = 3, Y = 2 on the screen	
6.	Set spot 1 cm from edge of screen	
7.	With spot as in 6, switch on the time-base and set speed to 100 ms/cm	

MEASURING VOLTAGE

Set the controls again as on chart of Fig. 5.4 so that you have a horizontal line on the screen. We will now use the CRO to measure the voltage of a battery. The stages are as follows:

(a) Set zero by connecting the two input (Y and E) leads together, and adjusting the Y-position control so that the horizontal line is at zero (centre of screen) as in Fig. 5.6.

(b) Now connect the battery as shown in Fig. 5.6 and adjust the volts/cm control until the line is deflected up a reasonable amount. Calculate the deflection from the screen graticule and multiply by the volts/cm setting to obtain the battery voltage.

(c) Repeat your calculation using (i) different volts/cm setting, and (ii) by reversing the leads on the battery.

To measure an a.c. voltage connect either a signal generator to the input of the CRO, or the secondary of a low voltage (about 5–10 V) mains transformer.

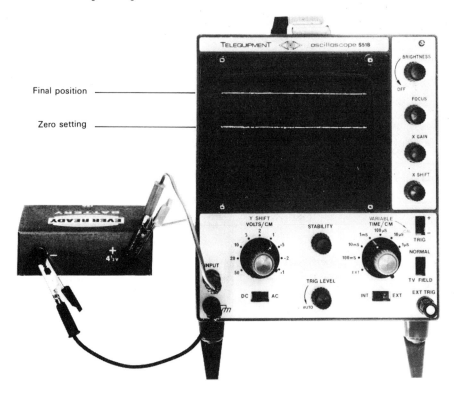

Fig. 5.6   Using a CRO to measure the voltage across a battery

If using a signal generator set the frequency to around 200 Hz, and adjust the output to around 1–2 V. Adjust the VOLTS/CM control of the CRO to give a trace of several cm high. If the display is not stationary adjust the TRIGGER CONTROL(S). You should now have a trace similar to that in Fig. 5.7.

(*Note*. If you are having difficulty refer to pp. 142–3 which should help you.)

The peak–peak voltage is best measured by using the Y-SHIFT to set the 'bottom' of the waveform on a graticule line, and using the X-SHIFT to move a peak to the centre line as shown. Measure from the graticule the peak–peak in cm, then multiply by the volts/cm setting to obtain the voltage.

The *amplitude* or peak value is, of course, half that measured.

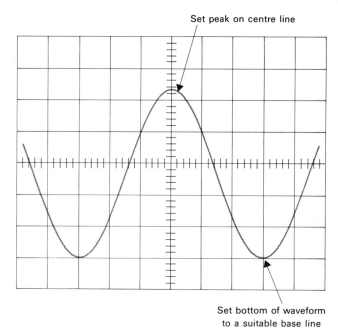

Set peak on centre line

Set bottom of waveform
to a suitable base line

Fig. 5.7 A voltage trace on a CRO

Change the frequency and output controls of the signal generator and do another set of measurements. Complete the table below.

Waveform	Gain (volts/cm)	Height (cm)	Volts peak–peak
1			
2			

MEASURING FREQUENCY

The CRO does not measure frequency directly. It can however measure the periodic time T of a waveform and from this the frequency can be calculated using the equation

$$f = \frac{1}{T}$$

Using the same arrangements as you did for the voltage measurement, adjust the signal generator† and/or the CRO so that you have about $1\frac{1}{2}$ cycles displayed on the screen as in Fig. 5.8. Using the Y-shift adjust the trace so that it is symmetrical about the X-axis, and use the X-shift to give a suitable reference point on one of the divisions on the time axis. Measure the time interval for one cycle as shown. Enter your readings on a table such as that below and calculate the frequency of the waveform. Compare with the frequency setting of the signal generator.

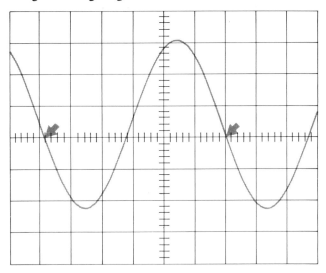

Fig. 5.8   The measurement of periodic time on a CRO

Time-base speeds (ms/cm)	1 cycle occupies cm	Periodic time T	Calculated frequency $f = 1/T$ Hz	Signal generator frequency setting (Hz)

Now change the frequency of the signal generator to a different value and also change the time–base speed (TIME/CM control) so that several cycles are displayed as shown in Fig. 5.9. To determine the frequency of this waveform you will probably find it easier to calculate the total time taken for a few cycles and divide by the number of cycles to find the time for one cycle. Enter your readings in a table and again compare your calculate frequency with the reading of the signal generator.

† If you do not have a signal generator these measurements can be carried out with a low voltage mains transformer, but, of course, only one frequency (50 Hz) will be available.

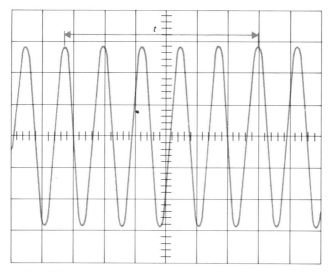

Fig. 5.9   Frequency measurement. Count the number of cycles in time *t*

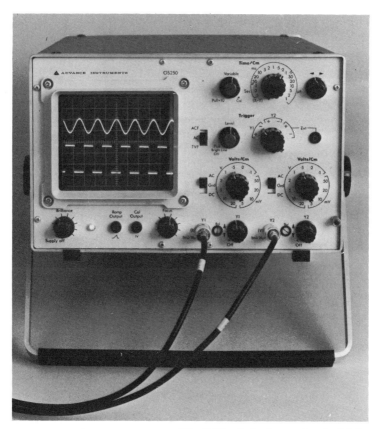

Fig. 5.10   A dual-trace (or double-beam) CRO

DUAL-TRACE OR DOUBLE-BEAM CROs _____

The CRO we have discussed is known as a single-beam instrument; it displays one trace. Although this is adequate for many purposes, the versatility of a CRO system is enhanced if two events can be displayed simultaneously. This can be achieved by using a *dual-trace* or *double-beam* CRO such as shown in Fig. 5.10 (p. 141).

Such an instrument can be thought of as two CROs in one. Two traces, known as Y_1 and Y_2 are produced on the screen which can be independently deflected in the vertical direction, the two deflections being controlled by *two* Y-amplifiers. These are called Y_1 and Y_2 or Y-upper and Y-lower, and there are, therefore, two VOLTS/CM switches and two Y-shifts. However, both spots are subject to the same horizontal deflection — they use the same time-base and X-amplifier and hence move across the screen 'in step' and at the same speed.

The advantage of such a system is that the *time-relationship* between two quantities can be observed and compared. For example, one trace could be used to display velocity and the other acceleration.

SOME COMMON FAULTS WITH THE CRO _____

Fig. 5.11 below shows some faulty traces on CRO screens and ways in which they may be remedied.

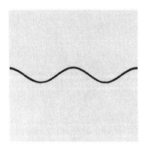 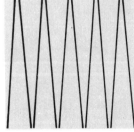 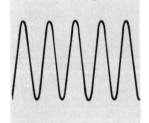

(a) Display amplitude too small. Change setting of Volts/cm switch, but don't go to a more sensitive range than 0.1V/cm. In which case increase output voltage of signal generator.

(b) Display amplitude too large. Change setting of Volts/cm switch, and if necessary decrease output voltage of signal generator.

(c) Too many cycles. Is Time/cm switch at 1 ms/cm? Are Variable(Vel) time-base controls in Cal position? Otherwise check signal generator frequency settings.

Fig. 5.11 (continued opposite)

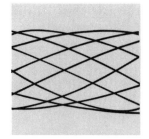

(d) Too few cycles — only part of it is seen. Check as opposite in (c) and additionally check that X-gain controls are in Cal position.

(e) Incorrect triggering Trigger Stability and Level controls not correctly set.

(f) Incorrect triggering. Follow instructions in (e).

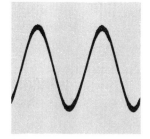

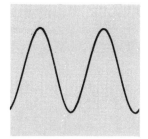

(g) Trace out of focus. Adjust Focus control and possibly Intensity control.

(h) Just right.

Fig. 5.11   Some typical faults with a CRO trace

EXERCISE 5

1)   The trace displayed on the screen of a CRO shows normally the relationship between (select one answer):

	Y-axis		*X-axis*
a	voltage	and	current
b	voltage	and	time
c	current	and	time
d	time	and	voltage

2)   With no input signal the spot appearing on a CRO screen is large and fuzzy. Which controls would you adjust to make it small and sharp?

3)   Which CRO controls would you adjust to move a spot on the screen to the coordinates X = 2, Y = 3?

4)   A sine-wave signal is applied to a CRO. The trace displayed is too small to see it clearly. Which control(s) would you adjust to make the display of greater height?

5)   One cycle of a sine wave is displayed on a CRO. To display several cycles which CRO controls would you adjust?

6)   With no input signal the trace on a CRO is a horizontal line on the screen. Calculate the deflection if a 15 V battery is connected to the input when the volts/cm is set to (a) 5, (b) 20. If the battery was reversed what would you observe?

7)   A sine-wave signal of 4 V peak–peak voltage and frequency 200 Hz is applied to a CRO. If the trace displayed is to be of the size shown in Fig. 5.12, calculate the controls settings you would select on: (a) VOLTS/CM switch, (b) TIME/CM switch.

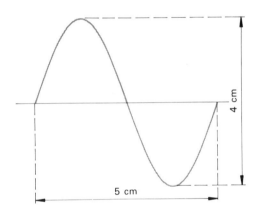

Fig. 5.12

MATERIALS

After reaching the end of this chapter you should be able to:

1. Recognise tensile, compressive and shear forces.
2. Define stress as force per unit cross-sectional area.
3. Solve simple problems involving direct stress.
4. Define strain as change of dimension per unit original dimension.
5. Solve simple problems involving strain.
6. Draw graphs of force against extension and stress against strain for an elastic material.
7. Define Young's modulus and relate it to the stiffness of the material.
8. Solve problems involving stress, strain and Young's modulus.
9. Sketch a complete load–extension diagram for mild steel.
10. Perform, describe and analyse the result of a standard tensile test to destruction.
11. Describe the form of stress–strain graphs for brittle and ductile materials.
12. Define the terms: ductility, brittleness, limit of proportionality and elastic limit.

ENGINEERING MATERIALS

The materials used in engineering can be grouped under three headings:

(a) the ferrous metals, which are composed mainly of iron and include all the steels, cast iron and wrought iron;

(b) the non-ferrous metals, which do not contain iron or contain it in very small quantities — for example, copper, brass, aluminium, magnesium, zinc, tin, titanium and the alloys of these metals;

(c) non-metallic materials, which include plastics, leather, rubber, fireclay, concrete, diamond and a variety of adhesives to name but a few.

PROPERTIES OF MATERIALS

Each material has certain properties or qualities as follows:

(a) strength, the ability to resist force — iron, steel and some aluminium alloys;

(b)   ductility, the ability to be drawn out into threads or wire — wrought iron, low carbon steels, copper, brass, titanium;

(c)   malleability, the ability to be rolled out into sheets or shaped by hammering — gold, copper, lead;

(d)   brittleness, the tendency to break easily or suddenly with little or no prior extension — cast iron, high carbon steel, concrete;

(e)   toughness, the ability to withstand suddenly applied or shock loads — certain alloy steels, some plastics, rubber;

(f)   elasticity, the property which enables a body to return to its original shape when forces which have distorted it are removed — rubber, mild and medium carbon and alloy spring steels;

(g)   hardness, the ability to resist surface indentation, wear or abrasion — high carbon steels, some alloy steels, carborundum, diamond.

DIRECT TENSILE, COMPRESSIVE AND SHEAR FORCES _____

Although there are many ways in which forces can be applied to an engineering component the simplest forms of application are those which have a direct effect. These are as follows:

(a)   Forces which pull and so tend to stretch the material are called *tensile forces.*

(b)   Forces which push and so tend to shorten the material are called *compressive forces.*

(c)   Forces which act parallel to each other and so tend to cause sliding of adjacent layers of the material are called *shear forces.*

For a tensile or compressive force to have only a direct effect its line of action must pass through the centre of area of each cross-section of the component. That is, it must act axially otherwise some other effect such as bending will occur (see Fig. 6.1).

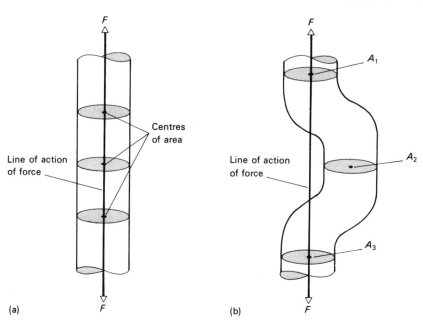

Fig. 6.1   Tensile forces: (a) direct loading, (b) indirect loading (bending would occur on sections such as A_2 where the line of action does not pass through the centre area)

To produce direct shear the shear forces must be applied in planes parallel and immediately adjacent to the cross-section under shear [see Fig. 6.2(a)]. If not, bending will also be caused [see Fig. 6.2(b)].

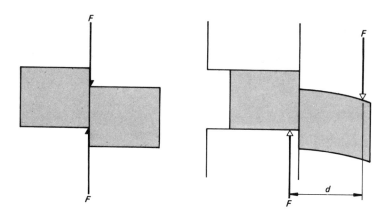

Fig. 6.2   Shear forces: (a) direct loading (line of action of forces coincides with plane of shear); (b) indirect loading (forces distant d apart cause bending as well as shear)

STRESS AND STRAIN

If a tensile force is directly applied, it will distribute itself uniformly over each cross-sectional area. The amount of force transmitted per unit of area is called the tensile stress. Thus

$$\text{Tensile stress} = \frac{\text{Tensile force}}{\text{Cross-sectional area}} \qquad [6.1]$$

This stress causes the component to stretch in the direction of the force. The extension per unit length is called tensile strain. Thus

$$\text{Tensile strain} = \frac{\text{Extension}}{\text{Original length}} \qquad [6.2]$$

Let

F = the applied direct tensile force (N)

A = area of the cross-section (m²)

l = original length of the component (m)

x = extension caused by F (m)

σ = tensile stress (N/m²)

ϵ = tensile strain

Then, from equation [6.1],

$$\sigma = \frac{F}{A} \text{ N/m}^2 \qquad [6.3]$$

and from equation [6.2],

$$\epsilon = \frac{x}{l} \qquad [6.4]$$

Since both x and l are measured in metres the units cancel and hence strain is simply a numerical quantity, that is, it has no units.

COMPRESSIVE STRESS AND STRAIN

When a direct compressive force F is applied to a component the latter will shorten slightly in the direction of the force. As in the case of tension, the compressive force will be distributed uniformly over the cross-sectional area withstanding the thrust, then

$$\text{Compressive stress } \sigma = \frac{F}{A} \text{ N/m}^2 \qquad [6.5]$$

and

$$\boxed{\text{Compressive strain } \epsilon \ = \ \frac{x}{l}}$$ [6.6]

where x = reduction in length caused by the compressive force F.

WORKED EXAMPLE 1

A cylindrical bar has a cross-sectional area of 400 square millimetres and a length of one metre. A direct tensile force of 16 000 N applied to the bar causes it to extend in length by 0.2 mm. Determine the stress in the bar and the strain.

SOLUTION

$$\text{Tensile stress } = \frac{\text{Load}}{\text{Area of cross-section}}$$

or, using equation [6.3],

$$\sigma = \frac{F}{A}$$

$$= \frac{16\,000}{400}$$

$$= 40\,\text{N/mm}^2 \quad \text{or} \quad 40\,\text{MN/m}^2$$

$$\text{Tensile strain } = \frac{\text{Extension}}{\text{Original length}}$$

or, using equation [6.4],

$$\epsilon = \frac{x}{l}$$

$$= \frac{0.2 \times 10^{-3}}{1}$$

$$= 0.0002$$

TENSILE TESTING _____

The methods for the tensile testing of metals are specified in *British Standard 18*. Part 1 deals with non-ferrous metals and Part 2 deals with steel.

The cross-section of the test-piece may be circular, square, rectangular or annular. However the commonest type is the circular section test-piece (Fig. 6.3) which has the gauge length equal to 5 times its diameter.

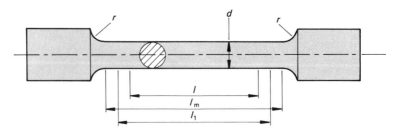

Fig. 6.3 The standard circular test-piece

Test-pieces vary in size and Table 6.1 shows the dimensions of British Standard test-pieces.

TABLE 6.1

Cross-sectional area A (mm^2)	Diameter d (mm)	Gauge length l (mm)	Minimum parallel length l_m (mm)[†]	Minimum transition radius r (mm)	Tolerance on diameter ($\pm$mm)
400	22.56	113	124	23.5	0.13
200	15.96	80	88	15	0.08
150	13.82	69	76	13	0.07
100	11.28	56	62	10	0.06
50	7.98	40	44	8	0.04
25	5.64	28	31	5	0.03
12.5	3.99	20	22	4	0.02

[†] The gauge length is given to the nearest 1mm and the minimum parallel length is adjusted accordingly.

METHOD OF TESTING

The test-piece is held in a testing machine by means of wedges, shouldered holders, etc. (see Fig. 6.7). It is pulled slowly in a controlled manner with the force applied axially to give direct loading. The test-piece is usually pulled until fracture occurs and the increasing values of load and the corresponding extensions are noted so that a load–extension graph can be drawn. A load–extension graph for wrought iron and low carbon steel is shown in Fig. 6.4.

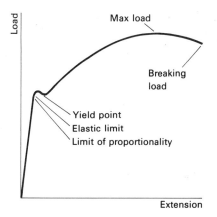

Fig. 6.4   A load–extension graph for wrought iron and low carbon steel

THE LIMIT OF PROPORTIONALITY AND THE ELASTIC LIMIT _

At zero load there is, initially, zero extension. As the load is increased the extension at first increases proportionately so that when load and extension values are plotted a straight line is obtained. The relationship continues up to a point, called the *limit of proportionality*, when the graph ceases to be a straight line. Just beyond this point is a second limit called the *elastic limit*, a point which needs very great care if it is to be determined accurately. Up to here the metal is completely elastic, so that if the load were removed the test piece would return to its original length. Beyond this point the metal is no longer completely elastic so that removal of the load now results in a small permanent extension (or permanent set).

YIELD POINT

At a load a little higher than the elastic limit the test-piece extends or yields suddenly by a comparatively large amount. This point is called the *yield point* and shows as a distinct kink in the graph.

MAXIMUM LOAD

Further increases in load are now found to be necessary to cause further extension but equal increments of load cause greater and greater amounts of extension and so the curve rises less and less steeply until the maximum load is reached.

Up to this point, the test-piece, as it stretched, reduced only very slightly in diameter, an amount measurable only by micrometer or vernier, and so the cross-sectional area has remained virtually constant. Now, at the maximum load, a 'neck' or 'waist' begins to form locally, its exact location depending upon minute structural defects within the metal. From now on the cross-sectional area reduces rapidly (Fig. 6.5) and so progressively less load is required to continue extending the test-piece.

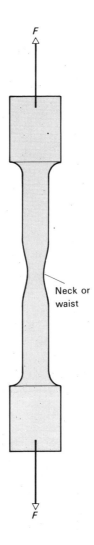

Fig. 6.5   A waist formed by extending beyond the maximum load

BREAKING LOAD

The curve of the graph is, therefore, now downwards as the extension continues, until eventually the test-piece breaks, usually with a cup and cone fracture as shown in Fig. 6.6. The load at which fracture occurs is called the breaking load.

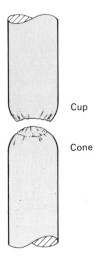

Cup

Cone

Fig. 6.6   A test-piece with a cup and cone fracture

MEASURING EXTENSIONS

Up to, and just beyond, the elastic limit the extension is measured by using an extensometer, an instrument which allows the extension to be measured very accurately (Fig. 6.7, p. 154). It is then usual to remove this instrument to avoid damaging it when the specimen fractures. The larger extensions beyond the yield point are now measured by using a pair of dividers and a steel rule.

STRESS–STRAIN GRAPHS FOR IRON AND STEEL

Following a tensile test the forces causing the extension of the test-piece are sometimes divided by the original cross-sectional area and the resulting extensions by the original (gauge) length of the test-piece. Thus a set of tensile stresses and their corresponding strains are obtained and plotting these values gives a stress–strain diagram.

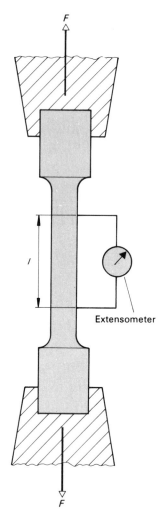

Fig. 6.7   Holding the test-piece in the testing machine

A stress–strain diagram is of more general use than a load–extension graph because the information it gives is not limited to the test piece used but it can be applied to any component made of the same material as the test piece. This is because stress refers to a standard area (1 m²) and strain refers to a standard length (1 m). Thus stress and strain refer to the same specimen size.

Stress–strain graphs are similar in shape to load–extension diagrams, and the stress–strain diagram for wrought iron and low-carbon steel will be similar in shape to Fig. 6.4. However, the important points on the graph give stresses instead of loads (Fig. 6.8).

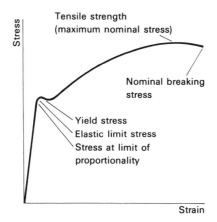

Fig. 6.8 A nominal stress–strain diagram for mild steel

Fig. 6.8 shows the breaking stress as being less than the maximum stress. This is impossible because the breaking stress must be the greatest stress to which the test-piece is subjected. The reason is that the cross-section does not remain constant as was assumed when calculating the stresses but it reduces in area as the test-piece is stretched. The reduction in area is not significant up to the yield point and it is very slight up to the point of maximum load. After this point the test-piece begins to form a waist and from then on the area reduces rapidly up to the point of fracture. If the loads had been divided by the *actual* cross-sectional areas to give true stresses a graph like Fig. 6.9 would be obtained, and we see that the true breaking stress is the greatest stress attained during the test.

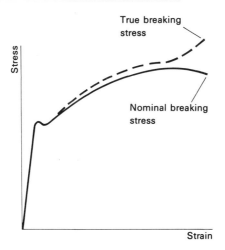

Fig. 6.9 A true stress–strain diagram for mild steel

The stress corresponding to the maximum load is called the *tensile strength* and it is useful for comparing the strengths of various materials in engineering design. Stress values beyond the tensile strength are never used and for all practical purposes the stress–strain curve of Fig. 6.8 is used instead of that of Fig. 6.9.

Machinery and equipment are never operated beyond the yield stress of the material because permanent distortion would then occur. In fact, designers often work to 50% or less of the yield stress to take account of unusual loading conditions which may occur when the equipment is operating.

WORKED EXAMPLE 2

A mild steel test-piece having a cross-sectional area of $100\,\text{mm}^2$ is subjected to a steadily increasing load and is seen to yield when the load reaches a value of $30\,000\,\text{N}$. (a) Calculate the yield stress of the mild steel. (b) Determine the diameter of a tie bar made from the same steel which will withstand a direct pull of $200\,000\,\text{N}$ if the stress in the bar is not to exceed half the yield stress.

SOLUTION

(a)   From equation [6.1],

$$\text{Yield stress for mild steel} = \frac{\text{Load at yield}}{\text{Area of cross-section}}$$

$$= \frac{30\,000}{100}$$

$$= 300\,\text{N/mm}^2$$

(b) $$\text{Permissible stress in the tie-bar} = \frac{300}{2}$$

$$= 150\,\text{N/mm}^2$$

Again, from equation [6.1],

$$\text{Area of tie bar cross-section} = \frac{\text{Load on tie bar}}{\text{Permissible stress}}$$

$$A = \frac{200\,000}{150}$$

$$= 1333\,\text{mm}^2$$

and

$$\text{Circular cross-sectional area} = \frac{\pi d^2}{4}$$

where d = diameter of the tie-bar

$$d^2 = \frac{4A}{\pi}$$

$$d = \sqrt{\frac{4 \times 1333}{\pi}}$$

$$= 41.2\,\text{mm}$$

PERCENTAGE ELONGATION AND REDUCTION OF AREA

If, after fracture, the broken parts of a test-piece are carefully placed together so that the fractured ends fit into each other (Fig. 6.10), the minimum diameter d_1 and the final gauge length l_1 can be measured by using calipers and steel rule. Two very important values can be found from these measurements. The first of these is the *percentage elongation*. This is the permanent elongation after fracture $l_1 - l$ expressed as a percentage of the original gauge length l. Thus

$$\text{Percentage elongation} = \frac{l_1 - l}{l} \times 100 \qquad [6.7]$$

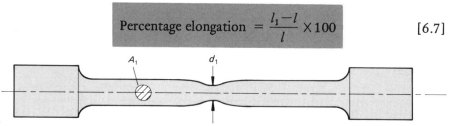

Fig. 6.10   Rejoining the parts of a test-piece for measurement

The second value is the *percentage reduction in area*, which is the maximum change in cross-sectional area $A - A_1$ expressed as a percentage of the the original cross-sectional area A; that is

$$\text{Percentage reduction in area} = \frac{A - A_1}{A} \times 100 \qquad [6.8]$$

These two values are a measure of the ductility of the material. Ductility is an important property. For example, a component having a complex shape may, when loaded, experience high stresses (stress concentrations) at sharp corners or sudden changes of section. If, however, the metal from which it is made is ductile, local yielding will take place in the regions of the high stresses thus reducing the stress concentrations. Thus components made from this metal, although it may not be as strong as a more brittle (less ductile) metal, may be better able to withstand shock loads.

WORKED EXAMPLE 3

A test-piece of circular section is pulled to destruction and its parts fitted carefully together again. The original gauge length was 80 mm and the diameter of the parallel length of the test-piece was 15.96 mm (see Table 6.1). After fracture the final gauge length was found to be 94 mm and the minimum diameter 12 mm. Determine: (a) the percentage elongation, and (b) the percentage reduction in area.

SOLUTION

(a)
$$\text{Percentage elongation} = \frac{94 - 80}{80} \times 100$$

$$= \frac{14}{80} \times 100$$

$$= 17.5\%$$

(b)
$$\text{Percentage reduction in area} = \frac{A - A_1}{A} \times 100$$

where
$$A = \frac{\pi \times 15.96^2}{4} = 200 \text{ mm}^2$$

and
$$A_1 = \frac{\pi \times 12^2}{4} = 113 \text{ mm}^2$$

then
$$\text{Percentage reduction in area} = \frac{200 - 113}{200} \times 100$$

$$= \frac{87}{200} \times 100$$

$$= 43.5\%$$

MODULUS OF ELASTICITY

Most engineering materials display some elasticity when first loaded. Up to the proportional limit of the elastic region the load is found to be proportional to the extension so that when these two quantities are plotted against each other a straight line is produced. Similarly stress is proportional to strain up to the limit of proportionality (which is approximately the elastic limit stress) for the material. Thus

$$\text{Stress} \propto \text{Strain}$$

or
$$\text{Stress} = \text{A constant} \times \text{Strain}$$

or $$\frac{\text{Stress}}{\text{Strain}} = \text{A constant}$$

The constant is known as the *modulus of elasticity* or the *elastic modulus*. If the specimen is in tension or compression, it is called *Young's modulus* and is denoted by the letter E, so that

$$\frac{\text{Stress}}{\text{Strain}} = E \qquad\qquad [6.9]$$

It follows from equation [6.9] that E is represented by the slope of the straight line portion of the stress–strain graph since the slope is given by the ratio of the vertical (stress) ordinate to the corresponding horizontal (strain) ordinate.

The unit of stress is N/m^2, and as strain has no units then the unit of E must be N/m^2. Different materials have different values of E, so that the modulus of elasticity when found can be useful in determining the kind of material from which a component is made. Values of E tend to be high and are usually expressed in GN/m^2 (giganewtons per metre squared, where the prefix giga, or G, represents the factor 10^9). Thus E for steel is about $207 \times 10^9 \, N/m^2$ or $207 \, GN/m^2$. Table 6.2 lists approximate values of E for various materials.

TABLE 6.2

Material	E (GN/m²)
Wrought iron	186
Steel	207
Cast iron	96
Aluminium and its alloys	70
Copper	124
Brass	103
Phosphor bronze	96
Magnesium and its alloys	45
Beryllium	300
Titanium alloys	100
Monel	175
Carbon fibre	130–190
Nylon	2.75
Rubber	0.035
Polystyrene	2.4–4.1
Polythene (low-density)	0.117–0.240
Polythene (high-density)	0.550–1.030

STIFFNESS _____

This is the property which enables a material to resist deformation. For members in tension or compression it is measured as the force required to produce unit change in length, so that

$$\text{Stiffness} = \frac{\text{Longitudinal axial force}}{\text{Change in length}} = \frac{F}{x}$$

The unit of stiffness is therefore newton per metre (N/m). From equation [6.9],

$$E = \frac{\text{Stress}}{\text{Strain}} = \frac{FL}{Ax}$$

so that

$$\text{Stiffness} = E \times \frac{A}{L}$$

Hence, if E for a particular material is determined by using standard test pieces in accordance with BS18, then that value of E may be considered to be a measure of the stiffness of that material.

WORKED EXAMPLE 4

An aluminium strut in the landing gear of an aircraft is subjected to a compressive force of 2800 N as the aircraft lands and it shortens correspondingly by 0.750 mm. Calculate the stiffness of the strut.

SOLUTION

$$\text{Stiffness} = \frac{F}{x} = \frac{2800}{0.750 \times 10^{-3}} = 3733 \times 10^3 \, \text{N/m}$$

STRESS–STRAIN GRAPHS FOR OTHER MATERIALS _____

So far we have discussed stress–strain diagrams for wrought iron and the low-carbon steels. Other materials behave quite differently when undergoing a tensile test and the way in which some of the more common engineering materials behave is discussed below.

THE HIGHER-CARBON STEELS _____

As the percentage carbon in the steel increases the yield point becomes less definite, and hence more difficult to determine until the carbon content is around 1% when the metal no longer yields suddenly and the load–extension curve shows a smooth transition from the elastic to the plastic regions. The test-piece does not form a waist and fracture is sudden, occurring at the maximum load (Fig. 6.11).

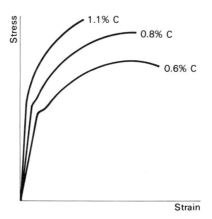

Fig. 6.11   A stress–strain graph for higher carbon steels

CAST IRON

Ordinary grey cast iron contains around 3.5% carbon, that is, more carbon than is contained in the steels where the upper limit is about 1.8%. Cast iron is very brittle and weaker in tension than the steels. It is not at all ductile and so does not form a waist before fracture. The stress–strain curve for cast iron is similar to that shown in Fig. 6.12.

Although cast iron is brittle, it has elastic properties. Extension is proportional to load within the limited elastic range indicated by the straight line portion of the graph. There is no yield point and fracture is sudden.

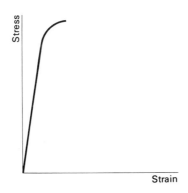

Fig. 6.12   A stress–strain graph for cast iron

COPPER

When copper is annealed (softened by heating and subsequent cooling) it is very ductile and yet does not have a yield point. A test-piece develops a waist, reducing· in cross-sectional area before fracture so that there is a smooth transition from the elastic to the plastic state. The curve reaches a maximum load then falls to a lower value before fracture takes place (Fig. 6.13).

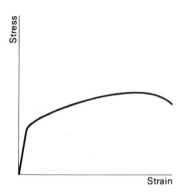

Fig. 6.13   A stress–strain graph for copper

BRASS

Brass is an alloy of copper and zinc, and generally is harder and stronger than copper but not so ductile. Fig. 6.14 shows the kind of stress–strain diagram expected of annealed brass. As with copper, there is a smooth transition from the elastic to the plastic state. The extension is less because of the lower ductility and there is little or no formation of a waist before fracture. The maximum load is the breaking load.

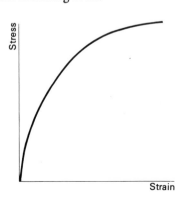

Fig. 6.14   A stress–strain graph for brass

ALUMINIUM ALLOYS _____

The alloys of aluminium are numerous and varied. The stress–strain curve shown in Fig. 6.15 is probably typical of many normal structural aluminium alloys as rolled, extruded or drawn, such as duralumin whose average composition is aluminium 95%, copper 4%, magnesium 0.5% and manganese 0.5%. The extension is less than that of mild steel and there is no definite yield point. There is slight local reduction in cross-sectional area before fracture due to the formation of a waist.

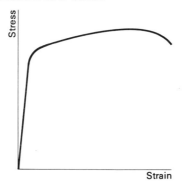

Fig. 6.15   A stress–strain graph for wrought aluminium alloys

PLASTICS _____

Stress–strain curves for plastics are not so predictable as they are for metals. The rate at which the load is applied, the humidity of the atmosphere and sensitivity to relatively small changes in temperature can all affect the behaviour of a plastic. However, on the assumption that there will be little variation in cross-sectional area as the load is applied to a test-piece the stress–strain curves for plastics, other than very hard brittle ones, will be similar in shape to the approximate load–extension curves shown in Figs. 6.16 to 6.19.

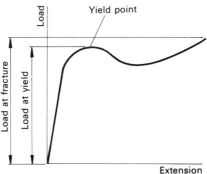

Fig. 6.16   A general load-extension graph for plastics

POLYETHYLENE ('POLYTHENE')

This strong, tough, flexible but relatively soft plastic has a stress–strain curve which is likely to resemble that shown in Fig. 6.17. Polyethylene has many uses including domestic articles such as buckets, squeeze bottles and other containers and coatings for electrical wiring. It has a tensile strength around 10–12 MN/m².

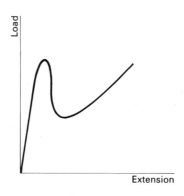

Fig. 6.17   A load–extension graph for polythene

NYLON

This material is a strong, tough, abrasion resistant (hard) plastic. The stress–strain curves for nylon are similar to that shown in Fig. 6.18. Nylon has a high yield and tensile strength (50–85 MN/m²) and a high percentage elongation. It is used to make gears, bearings, bushes, propellers, fan blades, screws and bolts and conveyor belting. Nylon in fibre form is used for ropes and toothbrush bristles.

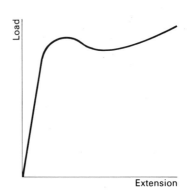

Fig. 6.18   A load–extension graph for nylon

POLYSTYRENE

This plastic, in the unmodified form, is very hard and brittle, has a high modulus of elasticity but a low percentage elongation. Its stress–strain curve is similar to that shown in Fig. 6.19, and therefore does not bear much resemblance to the general form of curve given in Fig. 6.16 for more ductile plastics. The tensile strength of polystyrene is fairly high, ranging from about 32 to 60 MN/m². Polystyrene is used in the forms of sheet and film for wrapping and in the form of rigid foam for packaging. It can be moulded to produce toys and household goods and, when modified by additives to give a tougher plastic, used in the manufacture of pipes and tubing.

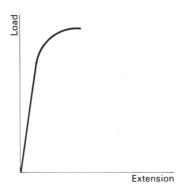

Fig. 6.19   A load–extension graph for polystyrene

SHEAR STRESS

Fig. 6.20 shows a bolt holding together two components which exert opposite forces F on the bolt. Then, as defined on p. 146 these forces are known as shear forces. The cross-section of the bolt in the plane in which F acts will be subjected to a shear stress whose magnitude is given by:

$$\text{Shear stress} = \frac{\text{Force exerted parallel to the cross-section}}{\text{Area of cross-section}}$$

i.e.

$$\tau = \frac{F}{A} \text{ N/m}^2 \qquad [6.10]$$

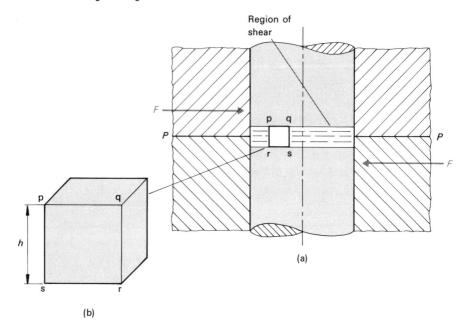

Fig. 6.20   (a) A bolt under the action of shearing forces, (b) a detail

WORKED EXAMPLE 5

The bolt shown in Fig. 6.20 has a diameter of 20 mm and the shear force F has a magnitude of 10 000 newtons. Calculate the direct shear stress in the bolt.

SOLUTION

$$\text{Area of bolt cross-section} = \frac{\pi \times 20^2}{4}$$

$$= 314\ \text{mm}^2$$

Then, using equation [6.10] gives

$$\text{Shear stress } \tau = \frac{10\ 000}{314}$$

$$= 31.8\ \text{N/mm}^2$$

$$= 31.8\ \text{MN/m}^2$$

DOUBLE SHEAR

A bolt or a rivet may be placed in either single or double shear (Fig. 6.21). For the rivet to fail in double shear it must fracture across both of the sections xx and yy. Hence

$$\text{Shear stress in double shear} = \frac{\text{Shearing force}}{2 \times \text{Cross-sectional area of rivet}} \quad [6.11]$$

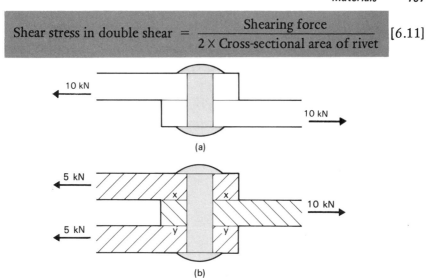

Fig. 6.21   Rivets in (a) single shear and (b) double shear

WORKED EXAMPLE 6

A rivet 10 mm in diameter is to hold three plates together (Fig. 6.22). If the loads applied to the plates are as shown find the shear stress in the bolt.

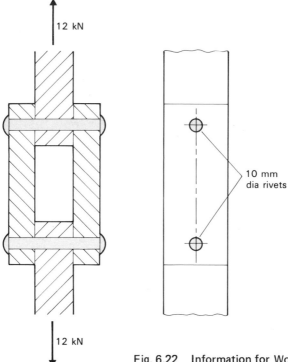

Fig. 6.22   Information for Worked Example 6

SOLUTION

Each rivet is in double shear. Hence

$$\text{Area resisting shear} = 2 \times \text{Cross-sectional area of rivet}$$
$$= 2 \times \pi \times 5^2 = 157 \, \text{mm}^2$$
$$\text{Shear stress} = \frac{12\,000}{157} = 76.4 \, \text{N/mm}^2 = 76.4 \, \text{MN/m}^2$$

SHEAR STRAIN

Again, we use the bolt in Fig. 6.20(a) as an example. The shear forces F acting in opposing directions cause the bolt material above and below plane PP to have a tendency to shear. This tendency, represented by a sideways movement of adjacent layers of the bolt material, is shown very much exaggerated in Fig. 6.23(a). If F is sufficiently small so that the shear stress is within the elastic limit, then the *shearing effect* or shear strain, as it is called, is small and the material will return to its original state when the force F is removed.

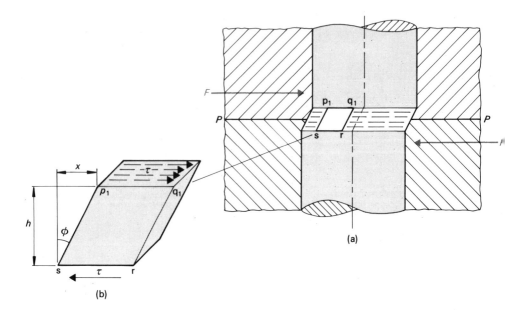

Fig. 6.23   The shear strain in a bolt

MEASUREMENT OF SHEAR STRAIN _____

Consider a small unstrained cube of the bolt material pqrs within the region of shear [Fig. 6.20(b)]. Let this cube have a height b units. If the bolt is now subjected to shear force F, the top and bottom faces of the cube are put under a shear stress τ equal to F/A (equation [6.10]). Because of this stress there occurs a sideways movement between the top and bottom faces equal to x. That is, the cube is distorted so that the face pqrs forms a parallelogram $p_1 q_1 rs$ leaning at angle ϕ to the vertical [Fig. 6.23(b)].

The shear strain is measured as the ratio of the sideways movement to the depth b; that is,

$$\text{Shear strain} \triangleq \frac{x}{b} = \tan \phi \triangleq \phi$$

where ϕ is measured in radians. (Note that ϕ is assumed small so that $\tan \phi$ is approximately equal to ϕ radians.)

EXERCISE 6 _____

1) Give three uses to which each of the following ferrous metals can be, or have been put: wrought iron, cast iron, mild steel, medium-carbon steel, high-carbon steel.

2) List six non-ferrous metals and give three engineering applications for each of them.

3) List six non-metallic substances used in engineering and give one application for each. State why each material was probably chosen for that application instead of choosing a metal substance.

4) Explain briefly and clearly what is meant by a direct effect of a force. Use freehand sketches to refer to tensile, compressive and shear examples.

5) Draw in good proportion, a load–extension graph for mild steel. Mark on the graph the load at yield and the maximum load.

6) A steel wire 6 metres long and 1.83 mm diameter is found to extend by 3.73 mm when a tensile load of 300 N is applied. Calculate: (a) the tensile stress, (b) the strain, (c) the stiffness.

7) Calculate the minimum diameter of round bar which is required to sustain a direct tensile load of 150 kN if the stress is not to exceed 124 MN/m^2.

8)   A test on a specimen of mild steel having a rectangular cross-section 75 mm by 25 mm gave an extension of 0.081 mm on a gauge length of 200 mm due to a load of 150 kN. Calculate the stress and the strain in the specimen.

9)   A hollow cast iron column of square cross-section has internal sides measuring 150 mm and it is to carry a load of 1000 kN. If the safe working stress is limited to 100 MN/m², calculate: (a) the area of metal required to carry the load, (b) the thickness of the walls of the column.

10)   A metal wire 1.60 mm diameter and 1.83 m long is subject to a load of 44 N and the extension is found to be 1.14 mm. Find Young's modulus of elasticity.

11)   A steel bar of circular cross-section is 2.00 m long and carries a load of 120 kN. If the maximum permissible stress is not to exceed 90 MN/m², determine the minimum diameter of the bar. If Young's modulus of elasticity is 207 GN/m², calculate the extension of the bar.

12)   A hollow vertical cast iron column 1.80 m long has an outside diameter of 300 mm and an internal diameter of 250 mm. It carries a compressive load of 500 kN. If E for cast iron is 96 GN/m², calculate: (a) the stress in the column, (b) the amount which the column will shorten, (c) the stiffness of the column.

13)   A tensile test-piece has a cross-sectional area of 400 mm² and a gauge length of 113 mm. It is loaded until fracture occurs, and the loads and corresponding extensions are tabulated below.

Load (kN)	0	20	40	60	80	100	120	140	148	
Extension (mm)	0	0.028	0.055	0.084	0.110	0.140	0.168	0.20	0.30	
Loan (kN)		148	150	160	170	180	190	200	180	180
Extension (mm)		0.40	0.45	0.66	0.80	1.00	1.28	2.0	3.2	fract.

Plot a load–extension graph using the following scales:

Load (vertical) 1 cm = 10 kN,

Extension (horizontal) 1 cm = 0.20 mm.

14)   Upon completing question 13 mark on the graph just drawn: (a) the probable limit of proportionality, (b) the yield point, (c) the point of maximum load, and (d) the breaking point. From the graph write down: (e) the value of the load at yield, (f) the maximum load, and (g) the breaking load.

15)   Referring to the tensile test-piece in question 13 and making use of information gained from solving questions 13 and 14, calculate: (a) the yield stress, (b) the tensile strength, and (c) the nominal breaking stress of the test-piece material.

16)   After fracture, the sections of the test piece of question 6 are fitted together and it is found that the minimum diameter at the waist is 18.5 mm and that the new gauge length has increased to 128 mm. Calculate: (a) the percentage reduction in area, and (b) the percentage elongation.

17)   A mild steel bar 15.96 mm in diameter and 80 mm long extended 0.060 mm under a tensile load of 30 kN. Calculate the value of E.

18)   During a tensile test on a bronze specimen with a diameter of 15.96 mm and a gauge length of 80 mm the following results were obtained:

Load (kN)	10	20	30	35	40	45	50	55
Extension (mm)	0.04	0.08	0.12	0.14	0.164	0.20	0.35	0.62

Draw the load–extension graph using the following scales:

Load vertical 4 cm = 10 kN,

Extension (horizontal) 1 cm = 0.05 mm.

From the graph and by subsequent calculation obtain the value of E.

19)   A bolt 10 mm in diameter is to hold two plates together. If the load applied to the plates is such that the bolt is in shear and its magnitude is 10 kN, calculate the shear stress in the bolt.

20)   Fig. 6.24 shows part of a link used in a machine tool. Calculate the maximum tensile stress in the members A and B and determine the shear stress in the rivets.

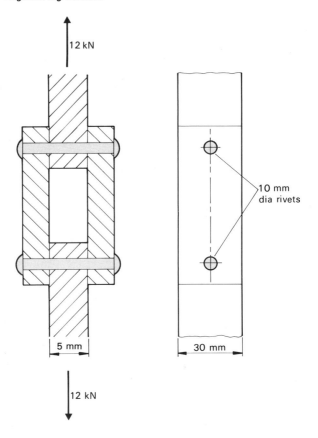

Fig. 6.2?

21)   The shear strength of a plate is $300\,MN/m^2$. Calculate the force required to punch a hole 40 mm diameter in a plate 7 mm thick.

22)   A mild steel bar has a rectangular cross-section of 90 mm by 20 mm. I? is 12 m long and its maximum allowable extension is to be limited to 2.5 mm. If the modulus of elasticity of the metal is $207\,GN/m^2$, find the maximum load it will be able to carry.

23)   A short cast iron column is to be a hollow cylinder 150 mm external diameter and it is to support an axial load of 360 kN. If the permissible stress is not to exceed $90\,MN/m^2$, find the inside diameter.

24)   A steel knuckle joint (Fig. 6.25) carries a tensile load of 90 kN. Find suitable dimensions for: (a) the diameter of the shank, D, if the permissible tensile stress is not to exceed $120\,N/mm^2$; (b) the diameter of the pin, d? if the permissible shear stress is not to exceed $80\,N/mm^2$.

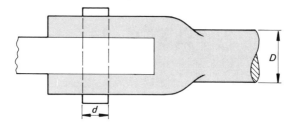

Fig. 6.25

25)   A pin in a forked joint is in double shear and the total load is 60 kN. If the maximum allowable shear stress is to be 70 MN/m², calculate the diameter of the pin.

26)   A certain member of the structure of a bridge shortens by 0.25 mm when under load. The cross-sectional area of this member is 20 000 mm² and it is 2.00 metres long. Calculate: (a) the stress in the member, (b) the force in the member. Take E for material to be 200 GN/m².

27)   A vertical bar 3 m long carries a load of 20 kN. If the extension in the bar is not to exceed 0.20 mm, calculate: (a) the stress in the bar, (b) the minimum cross-sectional area of the bar. Take $E = 200$ GN/m².

28)   The results below were obtained during a tensile test using a test-piece with a diameter of 15.96 mm and a gauge length of 80 mm. Find the value of E.

Load (kN)	5	10	15	17.5	20	22.5	25	27.5	30
Extension (mm)	0.01	0.02	0.03	0.035	0.041	0.05	0.088	0.15	0.23

29)   In a tensile test on a standard test specimen (diameter 11.3 mm and gauge length 56.5 mm) the following results were obtained: Yield load = 25 kN; ultimate load = 54.5 kN; diameter at fracture = 7.03 mm; length over gauge marks at fracture = 71.1 mm. Determine: (a) the yield stress, (b) the ultimate stress, (c) the percentage elongation, (d) the percentage reduction in area.

30)   In a tensile test the standard specimen used had a diameter of 22.56 mm and a gauge length of 113 mm. The following results were obtained: diameter at fracture = 11.58 mm; length over gauge marks at fracture = 142.5 mm. Calculate: (a) the percentage elongation, (b) the percentage reduction in area.

STATIC EQUILIBRIUM

After reaching the end of this chapter you should be able to:

1. Determine the resultant of two coplanar forces by drawing, giving magnitude and direction.
2. Use the polygon of forces to solve problems involving more than two coplanar forces.
3. Resolve forces.

FORCES

A force is required to move a body which was at rest or to cause a change in the motion of a body. Forces are measured in newtons (N), kilonewtons (kN) or meganewtons (MN).

Force is a vector quantity because it has both magnitude and direction, e.g. a force of 75 N acting vertically.

THE GRAPHICAL REPRESENTATION OF A FORCE

Vectors can be represented by straight lines drawn to scale. To represent a force the following information must be known:

(a)   its point of application (i.e. the point at which the force is applied to a body);

(b)   its magnitude;

(c)   its direction (line of action);

(d)   its sense (i.e. does it pull away from the point of application or does it push towards it).

WORKED EXAMPLE 1

Represent graphically the force shown in Fig. 7.1.

SOLUTION

(a)   Draw a horizontal line and mark on it the point A which is the point of application.

(b)   From A draw a line inclined at 50° to the horizontal to show the line of action of the force.

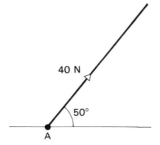

Fig. 7.1   Information for Worked Example 1

(c)   Choose a suitable scale to represent the magnitude. In Fig. 7.2 a scale of 1cm = 10 N has been chosen. A force of 40 N will be represented by a line 4 cm long. Hence from A mark off a distance of 4 cm.

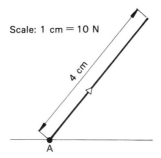

Fig. 7.2   The solution to Worked Example 1

(d)   Place an arrow on the line to show the sense of the force.

The force has now been represented graphically.

THE EQUILIBRIUM OF A BODY _____

A body is in equilibrium when it is at rest or when it moves with uniform velocity. A body can never be in equilibrium under the action of a single force. However if the body is acted upon by two equal and opposite forces it will remain in equilibrium (Fig. 7.3).

Fig. 7.3   A body in equilibrium under the action of equal and opposite forces

SYSTEMS OF FORCES _____

When two or more forces are applied to a body in an organised way they are called a system of forces.

RESULTANT FORCE _____

The resultant force is the single force which will have the same effect on a body as a system of forces.

WORKED EXAMPLE 2

Fig. 7.4 shows a system of forces. Find the resultant force.

8 N   22 N   20 N   16 N

12 N   25 N

Fig. 7.4   Information for Worked Example 2

SOLUTION

All the forces act in the same straight line. The resultant force is therefore the algebraic sum of the forces. Taking forces pulling to the right as positive and forces pulling to the left as negative we have:

$$\text{Resultant force} = 20 + 25 + 16 - 22 - 12 - 8 = 19\,\text{N}$$

Hence a single force of 19 N pulling to the right will have the same effect on the body as the system of forces.

THE EQUILIBRANT _____

The equilibrant is the single force which will put a system of forces in equilibrium. Since the resultant is the single force which has the same effect as the system of forces, the equilibrant will have the same magnitude as the resultant but it will be opposite in direction. Thus the equilibrant for the system of forces in Worked Example 2 is 19 N pulling to the left.

THE LINE OF ACTION OF A FORCE _____

The line of action of a force is that line along which the force acts. It is formed by extending the force vector in both directions (Fig. 7.5).

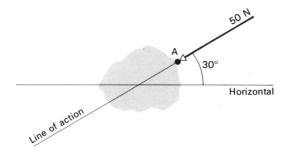

Fig. 7.5   The line of action of a force

The point of application of a force is the point at which the force is applied to the body on which it is acting.

COPLANAR FORCES

These are forces which act in the same plane.

THE PARALLELOGRAM OF FORCES

This is used to find the resultant of a pair of forces having different lines of action. The law of the parallelogram of forces states that:

If a body is acted upon by two forces F_1 and F_2 whose lines of action meet at O and which are represented in magnitude and direction by the vectors Oa and Ob (Fig. 7.6), then their resultant is represented in magnitude and direction by the diagonal Oc of the parallelogram Obca.

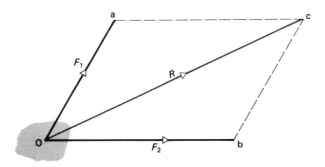

Fig. 7.6   The parallelogram of forces

WORKED EXAMPLE 3

Fig. 7.7 shows a body acted upon by the two forces F_1 and F_2. Find the resultant of these two forces and hence determine the equilibrant.

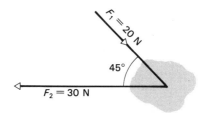

Fig. 7.7   Information for Worked Example 3

SOLUTION

In drawing a parallelogram of forces it must be remembered that both forces must either pull away or push towards the point of application. In this case the rule is achieved by drawing the parallelogram of forces as shown in Fig. 7.8. By scaling the resultant R is found to be 21.2 N acting at 42° to the 30 N force. Since the two forces both push towards the point of application the resultant will also act as a push.

The equilibrium E will be equal in magnitude but opposite in direction to R and it will therefore be as shown in Fig. 7.8.

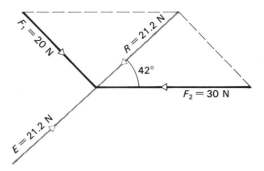

Fig. 7.8   The solution to Worked Example 3

THE COMPONENTS OF A FORCE _____

The parallelogram of forces can be used in reverse to replace a single force by two forces acting in any required directions.

WORKED EXAMPLE 4

A body is acted upon by a single force F of 40 N. Find by drawing the magnitude of the two components of this force which act in the direction Os and Ot as shown (Fig. 7.9).

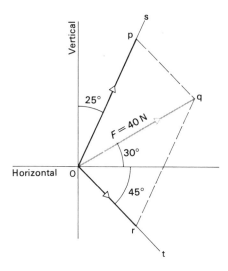

Fig. 7.9   The solution to Worked Example 4

SOLUTION

Draw Oq to represent force $F = 40$ N to some suitable scale such as 2 cm = 10 N. Draw Os and Ot in the required directions. From q draw lines parallel to Ot and Os to meet Ot and Os in points p and r respectively. Then Op and Or represent in magnitude and direction the required component forces. By scaling the figure it will be found that Op = 41.1 N and Or = 24.4 N.

RECTANGULAR COMPONENTS OF A FORCE _____

When the components of a force are at right angles to each other the parallelogram of forces becomes a rectangle of forces and the components of the force are then called rectangular components.

WORKED EXAMPLE 5

Fig. 7.10 shows a force $F = 80$ N acting at 60° to the horizontal. Calculate the vertical and horizontal (rectangular) components of this force.

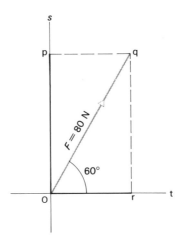

Fig. 7.10   Information for Worked Example 5

SOLUTION

Triangle Orq has angle Orq $= 90°$. Therefore
the vertical component which is represented by Op $=$ qr $=$ $F \sin 60°$
$$= 80 \times 0.8660 = 69.28\,\text{N}$$

the horizontal component which is represented by Or $=$ $F \cos 60°$
$$= 80 \times 0.5 = 40\,\text{N}$$

THE TRIANGLE OF FORCES _____

The triangle of forces states that:

If three forces acting at a point are in equilibrium they can be represented
in magnitude and direction by the three sides of a triangle taken in order.
The expression 'taken in order' means that the arrows representing the
senses of the forces must follow one another in the same direction, that
is, they must follow nose to tail.

WORKED EXAMPLE 6

A packing case which has a weight of 1000 N is suspended by means of two ropes fastened
to the same point on the case (Fig. 7.11). One rope makes an angle of 25° with the
horizontal and the other an angle of 45° with the horizontal. By drawing the triangle of
forces find the force in each rope.

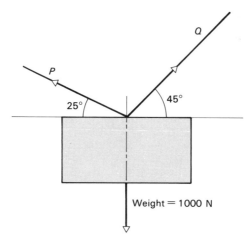

Fig. 7.11   Information for Worked Example 6

SOLUTION

Let *P* be the force in the rope inclined at 25° to be horizontal.

Let *Q* be the force in the rope inclined at 45° to the horizontal.

Referring to Fig. 7.12, draw to scale AB vertically downwards to represent the gravitational pull of 1000 N on the case. Place on AB an arrow indicating the sense of this force. The weight of the case has now been represented in magnitude, direction and sense. From b draw a line parallel to force *P* and from A draw a line parallel to force *Q*. These two lines intersect at C and ABC is then the required triangle of forces. Since the packing case is in equilibrium under the action of P, Q and the 1000 N force, the arrows on the force diagram must follow nose to tail. From Fig. 7.12, *P* = 752 N and *Q* = 964 N in the directions given.

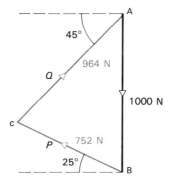

Fig. 7.12   The solution to Worked Example 6

THE POLYGON OF FORCES _____

The resultant of a number of coplanar forces acting at a point may be found by drawing a polygon of forces.

The theorem of the polygon of forces states that:
If a system of forces is to be in equilibrium the forces, when drawn out in order, must form a closed polygon.

WORKED EXAMPLE 7

A body is acted upon by five forces acting as shown in Fig. 7.13. (a) Determine, by drawing out the forces in order, whether or not the body is in equilibrium. (b) If not, what additional force would be needed to complete the polygon of forces and so provide equilibrium?

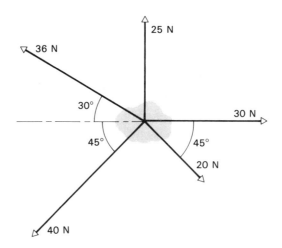

Fig. 7.13   Information for Worked Example 7

SOLUTION

The force diagram is drawn as shown in Fig. 7.14 starting with (say) the 30 N force then continuing in order with the 20, 40, 36 and 25 N forces so that the arrows follow nose to tail. These forces are represented by the vectors AB, BC, CD, DE and EF.

(a)   The diagram does not form a closed figure hence the system of forces is not in equilibrium.

(b)   The closing line is FA and this must therefore represent the equilibrant. That is, that force which will put the system of forces in equilibrium. This force scales 15.3 N and is at an angle of 2°9′ to the horizontal. The sense of the force is from F to A as indicated by the arrow.

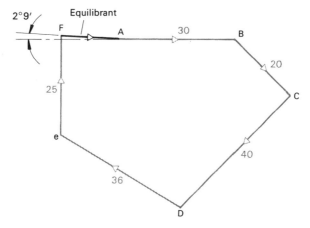

Fig. 7.14   The solution to Worked Example 7

EXERCISE 7 _____

1) Find graphically the magnitude and direction of the resultant of the two forces shown in Fig. 7.15.

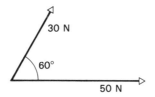

Fig. 7.15

2) Two tugs are towing a ship at constant velocity against a total resistance of 3000 N. The angles between the tow ropes and the direction of motion are 30° and 60° respectively. What is the tension in the tow ropes?

3) A shaft weighing 2000 N is hoisted by means of two chains attached to the shaft at equal distance from each side of its centre of gravity. The chains make an angle of 50° with the axis of the shaft. Find the tension in each chain.

4) A weight of 50 N is suspended by two strings of length 300 mm and 400 mm respectively attached to two points at the same level whose distance apart is 500 mm. Find the tension in the strings.

5) An arrangement for a crank and connecting rod is shown in Fig. 7.16. For the position given in the diagram determine the thrust in the connecting rod and the normal thrust R.

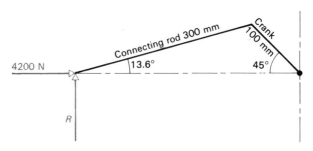

Fig. 7.16

6) A block of metal is set between guides so that it can only move horizontally (Fig. 7.17). Calculate the upward force on the top guide and the magnitude of the force which causes horizontal motion when a force of 350 N is applied as shown in the diagram.

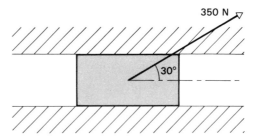

Fig. 7.17

7) The magnitudes and directions of four forces acting at a point O are shown in Fig. 7.18. Find the magnitude and direction of the resultant of this system of forces.

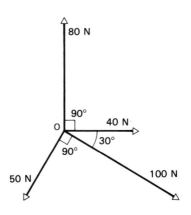

Fig. 7.18

8)   A point O is in equilibrium under the action of the five coplanar forces shown in Fig. 7.19. Find the magnitude of the forces *P* and *Q*.

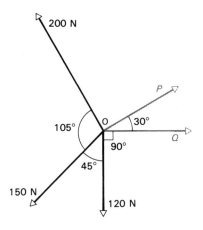

Fig. 7.19

9)   Find the resultant of the two forces shown in Fig. 7.20.

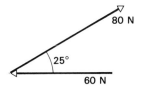

Fig. 7.20

10)   Fig. 7.21 shows the centre lines of members which meet at a joint of a structure. Find the forces in the members OA and OB in order that the joint shall be in equilibrium.

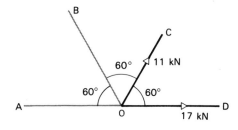

Fig. 7.21

MOMENTS

After reaching the end of this chapter you should be able to:

1. State that upward forces are equal to downward forces and that the sum of the clockwise moments equals the sum of the anti-clockwise moments at equilibrium.
2. Determine the reactions at the supports for a uniform, simply supported beam carrying point loads.
3. Solve simple beam problems involving reactions and the principle of moments.

THE MOMENT OF A FORCE

The moment of a force is measured by the product of the force and its distance from the fulcrum measured perpendicularly to the line of action of the force. Thus in both cases of Fig. 8.1.

$$\text{Moment} = Fd$$

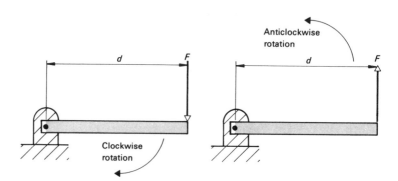

Fig. 8.1   Moment $= Fd$

In each case the force causes the lever to turn. At (a) the rotation is clockwise whilst at (b) it is anticlockwise. Moments may therefore be clockwise or anticlockwise.

In SI the unit of force is the newton and the unit of distance is the metre. Hence the unit of moment is newton $\times$ metre which is referred to as the *newton metre* (N m).

WORKED EXAMPLE 1

Fig. 8.2 shows a force of 200 N applied to a lever. Calculate the moment of the force about the fulcrum of the lever.

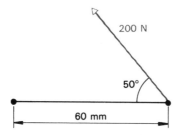

Fig. 8.2 Information for Worked Example 1

SOLUTION

Moment of the force about the fulcrum = Force × Perpendicular distance between the force and the fulcrum

As shown in Fig. 8.3,

$$\text{Moment} = 200d$$

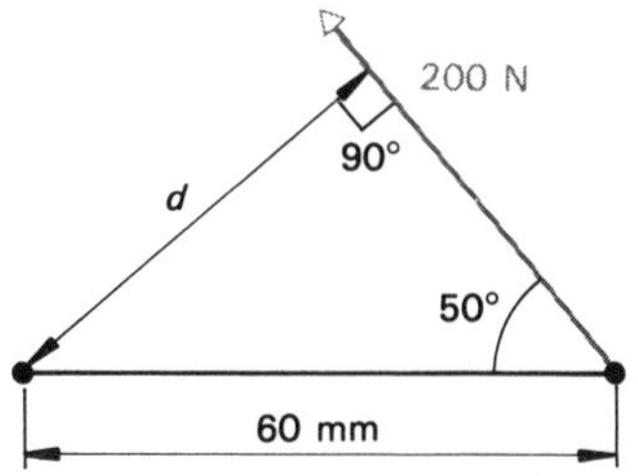

Fig. 8.3 The solution to Worked Example 1

The distance d may be found by trigonometry as follows:

$$d = 60 \sin 50° = 45.96 \text{ mm}$$

$$\text{Moment} = 200 \times 45.96 = 9192 \text{ N mm} = 9.192 \text{ N m anticlockwise}$$

HE NET MOMENT ON A BODY _____

When several forces act on a body the net or resultant moment is the algebraic sum of all the separate moments. This means that due account must be taken of the senses of the moments, i.e. whether they are clockwise or anticlockwise.

WORKED EXAMPLE 2

Calculate the resultant moment about the hinge for the forces acting on the lever show in Fig. 8.4.

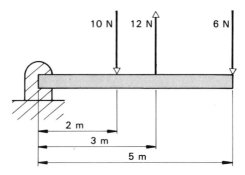

Fig. 8.4   Information for Worked Example

SOLUTION

Calling the clockwise moments positive and the anticlockwise moments negative,

Resultant moment $= (6 \times 5) - (12 \times 3) + (10 \times 2) = 14\,\text{N m}$

THE PRINCIPLE OF MOMENTS

This states that:

For equilibrium the sum of the clockwise moments must equal the sum of the anticlockwise moments.

WORKED EXAMPLE 3

Calculate the force F required to prevent rotation of the lever shown in Fig. 8.5.

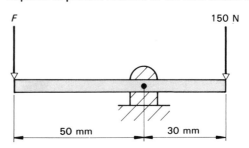

Fig. 8.5   Information for Worked Example

SOLUTION

Taking moments about O gives

Anticlockwise moment $= F \times 50 = 50F\,\text{N mm}$

Clockwise moment $= 150 \times 30 = 4500\,\text{N mm}$

By the principle of moments for equilibrium,

$$50F = 4500$$
$$F = 90\,\text{N}$$

CONDITIONS FOR THE EQUILIBRIUM OF A BEAM _____

For equilibrium of a beam the following conditions must apply:

(a) Sum of the upwards forces = sum of the downward forces.

(b) Sum of the clockwise moments = sum of the anticlockwise moments.

WORKED EXAMPLE 4

Fig. 8.6 shows a beam carrying three loads of 4 kN, 2 kN and 8 kN and supported at ends A and B. Calculate the reactions R_1 and R_2 at the supports.

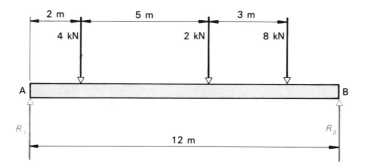

Fig. 8.6   Information for Worked Example 4

SOLUTION

The beam is at rest and therefore in equilibrium. Making use of condition (b) above and taking moments about end A through which R_1 acts gives

Clockwise moments = Anticlockwise moments

$$(4 \times 2) + (2 \times 7) + (8 \times 10) = R_2 \times 12$$

from which

$$R_2 = 8.5\,\text{kN}$$

Next taking moments about end B through which R_2 acts gives

Clockwise moments = Anticlockwise moments

$$R_1 \times 12 = (4 \times 10) + (2 \times 5) + (8 \times 2)$$

from which

$$R_1 = 5.5\,\text{kN}$$

Applying condition (a) to check the values of R_1 and R_2:

$$\text{Upward forces} = \text{Downward forces}$$
$$5.5 + 8.5 = 4 + 2 + 8$$

or

$$14 \, \text{kN} = 14 \, \text{kN}$$

Condition (a) is fulfilled, hence the values of R_1 and R_2 found by using condition (b) must be correct. Note that we could have used condition (a) to find R_1, once R_2 had been calculated.

WORKED EXAMPLE 5

A uniform beam is 8 cm long and weighs 120 N. It carries a load of 20 N at C, 3 m from A and x N at D, y m from A. The beam is supported at A and E. E being 6 m from A. If the reactions at the supports at A and E are 55 N and 115 N respectively, find the values of x and y.

SOLUTION

For a uniform beam the weight of the beam acts half way along the beam. The loading on the beam is then as shown in Fig. 8.7. Since, for equilibrium,

$$\text{Sum of the downwards forces} = \text{Sum of the upward forces}$$
$$20 + 120 + x = 55 + 115$$
$$x = 30 \, \text{N}$$

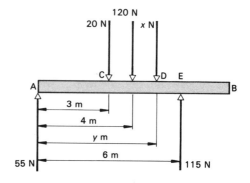

Fig. 8.7   Information for the solution to Worked Example 5

Also, for equilibrium,

Sum of the clockwise moments = Sum of the anticlockwise moments

Taking moments about A gives

$$(3 \times 20) + (4 \times 120) + 30y = 6 \times 115$$
$$60 + 480 + 30y = 690$$
$$30y = 150$$
$$y = 5\,m$$

Hence x is 30 N and y is 5 m.

EXERCISE 8 _____

1)   Fig. 8.8 shows a lever hinged at A. Find the force F needed to balance the load of 120 N. What is the force acting on the hinge pin?

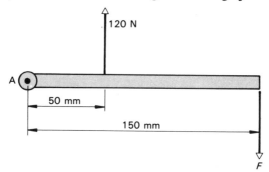

Fig. 8.8

2)   The lever shown in Fig. 8.9 is used for testing springs. Calculate the force F due to the spring and the reaction force R at the pivot when a load of 200 N is applied as shown.

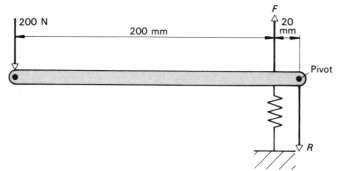

Fig. 8.9

3)   Complete the missing information in the table below (refer to Fig. 8.10).

	P (N)	Q (N)	R (N)	x (mm)	y (mm)
(a)	16	?	?	50	100
(b)	?	80	?	40	80
(c)	100	40	?	30	?
(d)	70	105	?	?	60

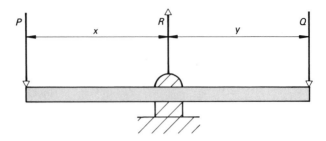

Fig. 8.10

4)   A uniform beam AB is 10 m long and weighs 2000 N. It is simply supported at the left-hand end A and at a point C which is 8 m to the right of A. Loads of 800 N, 2500 N and 1200 N are carried at points 2 m, 6 m and 10 m to the right of A respectively. Find the reaction at each support.

5)   A horizontal beam AB is 6 m long. It is supported at A by an upward vertical reaction of 1 kN and at C, 4 m from A. A load of 4 kN is placed 2 m from A and another load of 3 kN is placed at B. If the beam is uniform, calculate its weight.

6)   A beam 10 m long and weighing 3 kN is supported at its left-hand end and 2 m from its right-hand end. It carries loads of 1 kN, 0.8 kN, 1.5 kN and 0.6 kN at distances of 1.5 m, 4 m, 7 m and 10 m respectively from the left-hand end. Calculate the reactions at the supports.

7)   A uniform beam AB which is 8 m long is supported at each end and weighs 120 N. The beam carries loads of 20 N at C, 2 m from A and x N at D, y m from A. If the reactions at the supports at A and B are 85 N and 95 N respectively, find the values of x and y.

8)   A beam is loaded as shown in Fig. 8.11. Determine the values of the reactions of the supports at B and C.

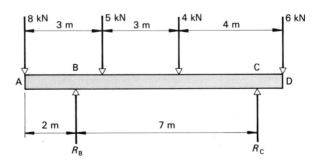

Fig. 8.11

VELOCITY AND ACCELERATION

After reaching the end of this chapter you should be able to:

1. Define angular velocity.
2. State the relation between linear and angular velocity.
3. State the relation between linear and angular acceleration.
4. Solve simple problems on angular velocity and acceleration.
5. State that velocity is a vector quantity.
6. Solve simple problems involving relative velocities.

LINEAR MOTION

DISTANCE

Distance is the length measured along any path, straight or curved, between two points. The SI unit of distance is the metre (m).

SPEED

Average speed is the distance moved in unit time. Hence

$$v = \frac{s}{t}$$ [9.1]

where

s = distance moved (metres)

t = time taken (seconds)

and v = average speed (metres per second)

Neither speed nor distance involve any particular direction and so are *scalar quantities.*

DISPLACEMENT

This is the direct distance between two points and it is specified by giving this distance and the direction in which it is measured. That is, both magnitude and direction are involved and hence displacement is a *vector quantity.* For example point B is displaced 10 metres horizontally to the right of a point A.

VELOCITY

The rate at which a body is displaced is called velocity so that

$$v = \frac{s}{t}$$ [9.2]

Equations [9.1] and [9.2] are identical, but [9.2] is concerned with vector quantities, i.e. velocity is a vector quantity.

ACCELERATION

Acceleration is the rate of change of velocity. Hence

$$a = \frac{v - u}{t}$$ [9.3]

where a = linear acceleration (metres per second per second)

v = final velocity (metres per second)

u = initial velocity (metres per second)

t = time taken (seconds)

WORKED EXAMPLE 1

At a certain instant a vehicle has a velocity of 20 km/h. It is given a uniform acceleration of 0.8 m/s² until its velocity is increased to 30 km/h. Determine the time taken in increasing the velocity.

SOLUTION

$$20 \text{ km/h} = \frac{20 \times 1000}{60 \times 60} = 5.55 \text{ m/s}$$

$$30 \text{ km/h} = \frac{30 \times 1000}{60 \times 60} = 8.33 \text{ m/s}$$

We have $u = 5.55$, $v = 8.33$ and $a = 0.8$. Using equation [9.3] gives

$$0.8 = \frac{8.33 - 5.55}{t}$$

$$t = \frac{8.33 - 5.55}{0.8} = 3.48$$

Hence the time taken is 3.48 seconds.

VELOCITY–TIME GRAPHS

(a)   The area under a velocity–time graph (Fig. 9.1) between any two time ordinates represents the distance travelled by the body during that period of time.

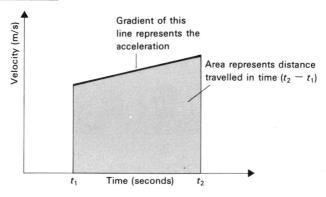

Fig. 9.1   A velocity–time graph for linear motion

(b)   For a body moving with uniform acceleration, the graph is a straight line whose gradient represents the acceleration.

WORKED EXAMPLE 2

A car at a certain instant has a speed of 15 m/s. It is given a uniform retardation of 0.5 m/s^2 until its speed is reduced to 10 m/s. Sketch a speed-time graph and from it determine the distance travelled during the retardation.

SOLUTION

Retardation is negative acceleration. Hence the speed-time graph will look like Fig. 9.2.

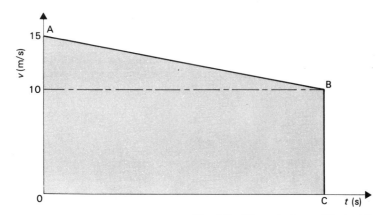

Fig. 9.2   The solution to Worked Example 2

The gradient of the straight line is

$$a = \frac{10-15}{t}$$

Since $a = -0.5$,

$$t = \frac{-5}{-0.5} = 10 \text{ seconds}$$

The distance travelled by the car is represented by the area of the trapezium OABC. Hence

$$\text{Distance travelled} = OC \times \frac{OA + BC}{2}$$

$$= 10 \times \frac{15+10}{2}$$

$$= 10 \times 12.5$$

$$= 125 \text{ metres}$$

The following equations connecting velocity, time, acceleration and distance travelled may be obtained by considering a velocity-time graph.

$$v = u + at \qquad\qquad [9.4]$$

$$s = ut + \tfrac{1}{2}at^2 \qquad\qquad [9.5]$$

$$v^2 = u^2 + 2as \qquad\qquad [9.6]$$

where

$$v = \text{final velocity (m/s)}$$
$$u = \text{initial velocity (m/s)}$$
$$a = \text{acceleration (m/s}^2)$$
$$s = \text{distance travelled (m)}$$

and

$$t = \text{time taken (s)}$$

WORKED EXAMPLE 3

A car moving with a uniform acceleration of 2 m/s^2 has an initial velocity of 3 m/s when first observed. Calculate: (a) its velocity 4 seconds later, (b) the distance it travels during those 4 seconds.

SOLUTION

We are given that $u = 3 \text{ m/s}$, $a = 2 \text{ m/s}^2$ and $t = 4 \text{ s}$.

(a)   Using equation [9.4] gives

$$v = u + at$$

$$v = 3 + 2 \times 4 = 3 + 8 = 11$$

Hence the velocity after 4 seconds is 11 m/s.

(b) Using equation [9.5] gives

$$s = ut + \tfrac{1}{2}at^2$$
$$s = (3 \times 4) + (\tfrac{1}{2} \times 2 \times 4^2)$$
$$= 12 + 16 = 28$$

Hence the distance travelled in the 4 seconds is 28 m.

ACCELERATION DUE TO GRAVITY _____

When bodies are allowed to fall freely in a vacuum near the earth's surface they all do so with the same acceleration of 9.81 m/s². The acceleration due to gravity is usually represented by the symbol g. The equations of motion for falling bodies may be obtained from equations [9.4], [9.5] and [9.6] by writing g for a. Thus

$$v = u + gt \qquad\qquad [9.7]$$

$$s = ut + \tfrac{1}{2}gt^2 \qquad\qquad [9.8]$$

$$v^2 = u^2 + 2gs \qquad\qquad [9.9]$$

WORKED EXAMPLE 4

A stone is dropped from a bridge into a river and takes 3 seconds to hit the water. Calculate (a) the velocity with which it hits the water and (b) the height of the bridge above the river.

SOLUTION

We have, $u = 0$, $g = 9.81\,\text{m/s}^2$ and $t = 3\,\text{s}$.

(a) Using equation [9.7] gives

$$v = u + gt$$
$$v = 0 + 9.81 \times 3 = 29.43$$

Hence the stone hits the water with a velocity of 29.43 m/s.

(b) Using equation [9.8] gives

$$s = ut + \tfrac{1}{2}gt^2$$
$$s = 0 + \tfrac{1}{2} \times 9.81 \times 3^2 = 44.15$$

Hence the bridge is 44.15 m above the water.

ANGULAR MOTION _____

When a body rotates about a fixed axis it is said to have angular motion.

ANGULAR DISPLACEMENT

This is the angle turned through by the rotating body and it is usually measured in radians.

ANGULAR VELOCITY

This is the angle turned through in unit time. That is

$$\text{Angular velocity} = \frac{\text{Angle turned through (rad)}}{\text{Time taken (s)}}$$

or, in symbols,

$$\omega = \frac{\theta}{t} \qquad [9.10]$$

where ω = angular velocity in radians per second (rad/s)

θ = angled turned through in radians (rad)

t = time taken in seconds (s)

Frequently the angular speed is stated in revolutions per minute (rev/min). It is then necessary to convert the speed to radians per second for the purpose of calculation.

$$1 \text{ revolution} = 2\pi \text{ radians}$$

$$1 \text{ revolution per minute} = \frac{2\pi}{60} \text{ radians per second}$$

If the body rotates at N rev/min,

$$\omega = \frac{2\pi N}{60} \text{ radians per second} \qquad [9.11]$$

WORKED EXAMPLE 5

The armature of an electric motor rotates at 5000 rev/min. Calculate its angular speed in radians per second.

SOLUTION

Since $N = 5000$ rev/min, from equation [9.11]

$$\omega = \frac{2 \times \pi \times 5000}{60} = 524 \text{ rad/s}$$

THE RELATION BETWEEN ANGULAR AND LINEAR SPEEDS ___

Let a body move in a circular path of radius r metres. In a time of t seconds let it move through an arc of length s metres corresponding to an angle of θ radians (Fig. 9.3).

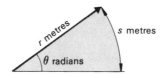

Fig. 9.3   Radial motion through s metres

Since the radian is defined as the angle subtended at the centre of a circle by an arc whose length is equal to the radius of the circle,

$$s = r\theta$$

Dividing both sides of this equation by t gives

$$\frac{s}{t} = \frac{r\theta}{t}$$

That is,

$$v = \omega r \qquad\qquad [9.12]$$

Equation [9.12] therefore relates angular and linear speed or velocity.

WORKED EXAMPLE 6

A pulley has a diameter of 300 mm and it rotates at 240 rev/min. It drives a belt which passes round the rim. Calculate the speed of the belt in metres per second.

SOLUTION

We are given $N = 240$ rev/min. From equation [9.11],

$$\omega = \frac{2\pi N}{60} = \frac{2 \times \pi \times 240}{60} = 25.13 \text{ rad/s}$$

The radius of the pulley is $r = 150$ mm $= 0.15$ m. Using equation [9.12] gives

$$v = \omega r = 25.13 \times 0.15 = 3.77 \text{ m/s}$$

Hence the speed of the belt is 3.77 m/s.

ANGULAR ACCELERATION _____

Angular acceleration is the rate of change of angular speed or velocity. Hence

$$\alpha = \frac{\omega_2 - \omega_1}{t}$$ [9.13]

where

α = angular acceleration in radians per second per second (rad/s^2)

ω_1 = the initial angular speed or velocity (rad/s)

ω_2 = the final angular speed or velocity (rad/s)

t = the time taken for the change in angular speed (s)

WORKED EXAMPLE 7

A wheel is given a uniform acceleration from rest. After 5 seconds it has an angular speed of 35 rad/s.

(a)   Calculate the angular acceleration of the wheel.

(b)   If the wheel continues to accelerate uniformly at the same rate determine its angular speed after a further 10 seconds.

SOLUTION

(a)   We have $\omega_1 = 0$, $\omega_2 = 35$ rad/s, $t = 5$ s. From equation [9.13]

$$\alpha = \frac{\omega_2 - \omega_1}{t} = \frac{35 - 0}{5} = 7 \text{ rad/s}^2$$

(b)   We have $\omega_1 = 35$ rad/s, $\alpha = 7$ rad/s^2 and $t = 10$ s. To find ω_2 we use equation [9.13]:

$$\alpha = \frac{\omega_2 - \omega_1}{t}$$

Transposing the equation to make ω_2 the subject, we have

$$\omega_2 = \alpha t + \omega_1$$
$$= (7 \times 10) + 35 = 105 \text{ rad/s}$$

Alternatively we may consider the whole time to be 15 seconds and ω_1 is then 0.

$$\omega_2 = (7 \times 15) + 0 = 105 \text{ rad/s}$$

THE RELATION BETWEEN LINEAR AND ANGULAR ACCELERATION

If a body starts from rest and reaches an angular velocity of ω rad/s in t seconds, then

$$\alpha = \frac{\omega}{t}$$

Equation [9.12] gives

$$v = \omega r$$

Dividing both sides by t, we have

$$\frac{v}{t} = r \cdot \frac{\omega}{t}$$

$$a = r\alpha \qquad\qquad [9.14]$$

Equation [9.14] relates linear and angular acceleration.

WORKED EXAMPLE 8

Starting from rest a road vehicle having wheels 1 m diameter reaches a speed of 8 m/s in 10 seconds. Calculate the angular acceleration of the wheels.

SOLUTION

We have $u = 0$, $v = 8$ m/s and $t = 10$ s. Using equation [9.3] to find the linear acceleration gives

$$a = \frac{v-u}{t} = \frac{8-0}{10} = 0.8 \text{ m/s}^2$$

Using equation [9.14], we have

$$a = r\alpha$$

or

$$\alpha = \frac{a}{r} = \frac{0.8}{0.5} = 1.6 \text{ rad/s}^2$$

Hence the angular acceleration of the wheels is 1.6 rad/s².

SPEED–TIME GRAPHS FOR ANGULAR MOTION

Speed–time graphs for angular motion are very similar to those used for linear motion.

(a)   The area under the graph (Fig. 9.4) between any two time ordinates represents the angle turned through (in radians) by the rotating body during that period of time.

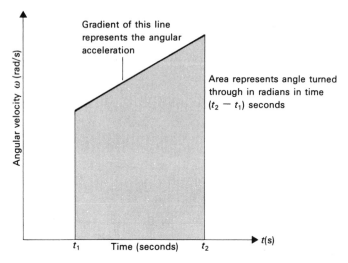

Fig. 9.4   A velocity–time graph for angular motio

(b)   For a body rotating with uniform angular acceleration the graph is a straight line whose gradient represents the angular acceleration.

WORKED EXAMPLE 9

A flywheel revolving at 20 rad/s has its speed increased uniformly to 40 rad/s in 1 min.

(a)   Sketch a speed–time graph.

(b)   From the graph find the angular acceleration for the flywheel.

(c)   Determine the total angle turned through in this time of 1 min, and hence calculate the total number of revolutions made by the flywheel.

SOLUTION

(a)   The speed–time graph is shown in Fig. 9.5.

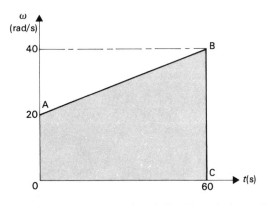

Fig. 9.5   The solution to Worked Example

(b)   Gradient of graph $= \dfrac{40-20}{60} = 0.33$ rad/s^2.

(c)   The total angle turned through is given by the area of the trapezium OABC. Hence

$$\theta = 60 \times \dfrac{20+40}{2} = 60 \times 30 = 1800 \text{ radians}$$

Since   1 revolution $= 2\pi$ radians

$$\text{Total number of revolutions} = \dfrac{1800}{2\pi} = 286$$

The following equations connecting angular velocity, time, angular acceleration and angle turned through may be obtained by considering a speed–time graph:

$$\omega_2 = \omega_1 + \alpha t \qquad\qquad\qquad\qquad [9.15]$$
$$\theta = \omega_1 t + \tfrac{1}{2}\alpha t^2 \qquad\qquad\qquad [9.16]$$
$$\omega_2{}^2 = \omega_1{}^2 + 2\alpha\theta \qquad\qquad\qquad [9.17]$$

where $\omega_1 =$ initial angular velocity (rad/s)

                  $\omega_2 =$ final angular velocity (rad/s)

                  $\theta =$ angle turned through (rad)

                  $\alpha =$ angular acceleration (rad/s^2)

                  $t =$ time taken (s)

On comparing equations [9.4], [9.5] and [9.6] with equations [9.15], [9.16] and [9.17] we see that they are similar in form.

WORKED EXAMPLE 10

A wheel has an initial angular velocity of 10 rad/s and a final velocity of 100 rad/s. If the angular acceleration is 6 rad/s^2, calculate: (a) the angle turned through during the change of velocity, (b) the time taken for the change.

SOLUTION

(a)   Using equation [9.17] gives

$$\omega_2{}^2 = \omega_1{}^2 + 2\alpha\theta$$

and substituting gives

$$100^2 = 10^2 + (2 \times 6 \times \theta)$$
$$10\,000 = 100 + 12\theta$$
$$\theta = \dfrac{9900}{12} = 825 \text{ radians}$$

(b)   Using equation [9.15] gives

$$\omega_2 = \omega_1 + \alpha t$$

and substituting gives

$$100 = 10 + 6t$$

$$t = \frac{90}{6} = 15 \, \text{seconds}$$

RELATIVE VELOCITY

Any vector quantity such as velocity can be represented by a straight line
The length of the line drawn to a suitable scale represents the magnitude o
the velocity and its direction is given by the direction of the line. Such a lin
is called a *vector*.

Suppose a bullet B is fired from a rifle at 1000 m/s horizontally to the right
Using small letters and starting with the point r (to represent the rifle R a
the fixed point or datum) a line rb is drawn horizontally to the right. Th
length of rb represents, to some suitable scale, the magnitude of 1000 m/
(Fig. 9.6).

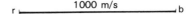

Fig. 9.6   The vector representation of velocity of *B* relative to *A*

Note that the letter at the starting point of any vector represents the poin
or body to which the motion is relative, in this case the rifle R.

THE REVERSAL OF A VECTOR

If a person could travel with the bullet B in the above example, the rifle
would appear to the person to be travelling at 1000 m/s to the left. Henc
the same vector (Fig. 9.6) read as br represents the velocity of the rifl
relative to the bullet B. Thus all vectors are reversible.

WORKED EXAMPLE 11

Two trains A and B are travelling on parallel tracks in opposite directions. Train A
travelling at 20 m/s eastwards and train B at 60 m/s westwards both relative to the trac
T. Represent these velocities vectorially and determine the velocity of (a) B relative t
A and (b) A relative to B.

SOLUTION

Since the tracks are parallel to each other in an east–west direction the vectors, when drawn, will fall in line with each other.

(a)   Draw vector ta to represent the velocity of A relative to the track T using a suitable scale to represent the magnitude of 20 m/s (Fig. 9.7). Next draw vector tb to repre- sent the velocity of b relative to T. Then the velocity of B relative to A is given by the vector ab. That is, the velocity of B relative to A is 80 m/s in the direction a to b (i.e. westwards).

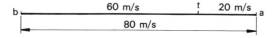

Fig. 9.7   The solution to Worked Example 11

(b)   The velocity of A relative to B is given by the vector ba; that is, 80 m/s in the direction b to a (i.e. eastwards).

WORKED EXAMPLE 12

Two cars P and Q are travelling along two different roads. The roads are set at an angle of 30° to each other and meet at junction M. Car P has a velocity of 30 km/h and car Q a velocity of 50 km/h relative to their respective roads in the direction shown (Fig. 9.8). Draw the velocity diagram for the two cars and by measurement and calculation, find the velocity of Q relative to P.

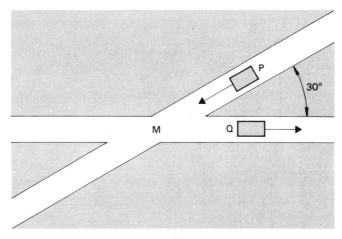

Fig. 9.8   Information for Worked Example 12

SOLUTION

Let M be the datum point relative to which the cars are moving. (Any point nearby on the earth's surface would do equally well.)

Method

Draw vector mp to represent in magnitude and direction the velocity of P relative to M. Draw vector mq to represent similarly the velocity of Q relative to M (Fig. 9.9). Then the velocity of Q relative to P is represented by vector pq. This scales 77.45 km/h in direction p to q at an angle θ of 19.6° to the road along which Q is travelling.

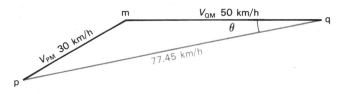

Fig. 9.9   The solution to Worked Example 12

EXERCISE 9

1)   A car accelerates from rest at 2 m/s² during a period of 5 seconds. Find the distance travelled during this acceleration.

2)   A train accelerates from rest at 0.2 m/s². Find the time taken and the distance travelled when the speed reaches 100 km/h.

3)   A car starts from rest and uniformly accelerates to a speed of 14 m/s in 20 seconds. The speed then falls uniformly to 10 m/s. The brakes are then applied to bring the car to rest in 3 s. The total distance travelled is 2000 m. Find: (a) the distance travelled whilst accelerating, (b) the distance travelled whilst braking, (c) the time taken for the entire journey.

4)   A road vehicle at a given instant has a speed of 6 m/s. It is given a uniform retardation of 0.9 m/s² until its speed is reduced to 3 m/s. Find: (a) the time taken in reducing speed, (b) the distance travelled during retardation.

5)   A vehicle is accelerated at 1.5 m/s² from a speed of 8 m/s. Calculate: (a) the time required to attain a speed of 25 m/s, (b) the distance travelled in this time.

6)   A lift, starting from rest, increases speed uniformly for the first 10 s until a speed of 3 m/s is reached. This speed then remains constant for the next 6 s and finally the lift is brought to rest in a further 8 s of uniform retardation. Determine: (a) the initial acceleration, (b) the final retardation, (c) the height travelled.

7)   A turbine rotor revolves at 628 rad/s. What is the speed of the rotor in revolutions per minute? (Assume $\pi = 3.14$.)

8)   A pulley having an effective diameter of 300 mm is driven by a vee-belt at 360 rev/min. Calculate the linear speed of the belt correct to two places of decimals. (Assume $\pi = 3.14$.)

9)   A car has road wheels which are 520 mm diameter. If the car is accelerating linearly at 1.5 m/s², calculate, correct to two places of decimals, the angular acceleration of the road wheels.

10)   The flywheel of an engine starts from rest and, accelerating uniformly reaches a speed of 540 rev/min in 10 s. Calculate its angular acceleration. (Assume $\pi = 3.14$.)

11)   A flywheel has an initial angular velocity of 20 rad/s and a uniform angular acceleration of 4 rad/s². Assuming that this acceleration is maintained, determine the time required for the flywheel to rotate through 400 radians.

12)   The winding drum of a crane has an effective diameter of 300 mm. A lifting cable is wound round the drum and from its free end is suspended a hook. If the drum, initially at rest, begins to rotate so as to raise the hook, accelerating at 1 rad/s², calculate: (a) the angle turned through by the drum in 5 seconds, (b) the angular velocity of the drum at the end of this time, (c) the corresponding linear distance lifted by the hook and (d) the linear velocity of the hook at the end of the 5 second period.

13)   Two trains, A and B, are travelling on parallel tracks in opposite directions. Train A is travelling at 30 m/s westwards and train B at 25 m/s eastwards both relative to the track T. Draw the velocity diagram and from it determine: (a) the velocity of train A relative to train B, (b) the velocity of train B relative to train A.

14)   An overhead gantry crane C is travelling at 2.5 m/s along the workshop W in an easterly direction. At the same time the crab from which the crane hook H is suspended is moving across the crane at 1 m/s in a southerly direction. Draw the velocity diagram, and from it determine in magnitude and direction, the velocity of the hook relative to the workshop.

15)   A wheel 2 metres diameter, with centre C rolls along a level track T from left to right with a linear velocity of 6 m/s relative to T. Fixed to the outside edge of the rim of the wheel is a point P. Draw the velocity diagram and determine the velocity of P relative to the track when: (a) P is in contact with the track, (b) the wheel has rolled through 60° from position (a), (c) P is at the topmost point of the wheel.

(*Hint.* The direction of the velocity of P relative to C will always be at right angles to the radius PC.)

16)   Two cars R and S set off from a junction J along two straight roads. Car R travels due north at 40 km/h and car S due east at 60 km/h. Draw the velocity diagram and find the velocity of S relative to R. Give the magnitude of the velocity to the nearest kilometre per hour.

FORCE AND ACCELERATION

After reaching the end of this chapter you should be able to:

1. *State Newton's first law of motion.*
2. *State Newton's second law of motion.*
3. *Solve problems using* $F = ma$.
4. *State that when a force acts on one body there must be an equal and opposite force on another body.*

NEWTON'S LAWS OF MOTION

These are statements concerning the way bodies behave when subjected to systems of forces. They are based on acute observation and experimentation. All our experience of natural phenomena tends to confirm that they are correct.

NEWTON'S FIRST LAW

A body will remain at rest or will continue to move with uniform motion unless acted upon by a resultant external force.

RESULTANT EXTERNAL FORCE

This will be either a single force acting alone or the resultant of several forces acting simultaneously. The force is one that is applied *to* the body from some source outside the body. That is, it is an *external* force.

INERTIA

The reason why a body behaves in accordance with Newton's first law is because of *inertia*. Inertia is a property which all bodies possess causing them to resist a change of motion and, therefore, enabling them to stay at rest or, if already moving, to go on moving uniformly in a straight line without the application of a force.

MOMENTUM

It is easier to set in motion a small boat than a large tanker. Similarly far greater distances are required in which to bring to rest a tanker than are needed for a small boat. The massive tanker is said to possess more *momentum* than the boat.

Momentum is defined as the product of mass and velocity

That is,

Momentum = Mass × Velocity = *mv*

When two bodies of different mass are acted upon by the same force for the same length of time the lighter one will attain a higher velocity than the heavier one but the momentum that each gains will be the same.

FORCE AND MOMENTUM

The relationship between force and momentum is expressed by Newton's second law.

NEWTON'S SECOND LAW

The rate of change of momentum of a body is proportional to the applied force and takes place in the direction in which the force acts.

If a force of F units acts on a body of mass m kilograms for a time of t seconds so that the velocity of the body changes uniformly from u metres per second to v metres per second,

$$\text{Rate of change of momentum} = \frac{\text{Change of momentum}}{\text{Time taken}}$$

$$= \frac{mv - mu}{t}$$

$$= \frac{m(v - u)}{t}$$

But

$$\frac{v - u}{t} = a$$

So that   Rate of change of momentum $= ma$

and according to Newton's second law, force is proportional to rate of change of momentum. Then

$$F \propto ma \quad \text{or} \quad F = kma \quad \text{where } k \text{ is a constant}$$

THE UNIT OF FORCE

The equation $F = kma$ enables the unit of force to be defined in SI. The unit of force is chosen as that force which will give to a mass of 1 kg an acceleration of 1 metre per second per second. Upon substituting in the equation $F = kma$ we have $1 = k \times 1 \times 1$, so that $k = 1$. This unit of force is called the newton (N) hence when F is in newtons, m is in kilograms and a is in metres per second per second.

$$F = ma \qquad\qquad [10.1]$$

MASS AND INERTIA

The mass of a body is usually defined as the quantity of matter in the body, but this, in practice, is impossible to determine. All bodies however, possess inertia as a consequence of their mass and a force is necessary to overcome the inertia of the body, that is to accelerate it. Thus the greater the force needed to be applied to give a body a particular acceleration, the more massive that body is considered to be. The mass of a body determined in this way is sometimes referred to as the *inertial mass* of the body.

WORKED EXAMPLE 1

Two bodies A and B are each given an acceleration of 8 m/s². To do this a force of 24 N had to be applied to A and a force of 72 N to B. What is the mass of each body?

SOLUTION

From equation [10.1],

$$F = ma$$

Therefore

$$\text{Mass of A} = \frac{\text{Force to overcome inertia of A}}{\text{Acceleration of A}}$$

$$= \frac{24}{8} = 3 \text{ kg}$$

Similarly

$$\text{Mass of B} = \frac{\text{Force to overcome inertia of B}}{\text{Acceleration of B}}$$

$$= \frac{72}{8}$$

$$= 9 \text{ kg}$$

THE WEIGHT OF A BODY

The weight of a body is the pull exerted on it by the earth's gravitational attraction. When bodies are allowed to fall freely in a vacuum near to the earth's surface they all do so with the same acceleration of 9.81 m/s² caused by this gravitational attraction. Applying equation [10.1] gives

Gravitational force or 'weight' of body = Mass of body × Acceleration

$$W = m \times 9.81$$

The acceleration of 9.81 m/s² caused by the earth's pull is denoted by the symbol g so that it is usual to write

$$W = mg \qquad\qquad [10.2]$$

ACTION AND REACTION

When a push is applied to an immovable object, say a wall, the wall reacts with an equal and opposite push. Similarly if the push is applied to a body which is free to move this body will exert an equal and opposite push in the form of an inertia reaction as it is accelerated by the force. The same applies if pushes are replaced by pulls.

Newton embodied these facts in his third law as follows:

NEWTON'S THIRD LAW

To every action there is an equal and opposite reaction.

WORKED EXAMPLE 2

A body has a weight of 562 N on earth. (a) What force is required to give it an acceleration of 8 m/s²? (b) What will be the inertia reaction of the body when given this acceleration?

SOLUTION

(a)   From equation [10.2]

$$W = mg$$

Therefore

$$\text{Mass of body} = m = \frac{W}{g} = \frac{562}{9.81} = 57.29\,\text{kg}$$

From equation [10.1]

$$F = ma$$

Therefore

$$\text{Accelerating force } F = 57.29 \times 8 = 458.3\,\text{N}$$

(b)   The inertia reaction of the body will, in accordance with Newton's third law, equal the force applied to the body and therefore is equal to 458.3 N.

WORKED EXAMPLE 3

A lift ascends with a uniform acceleration of $3\,\text{m/s}^2$ for a few seconds. It then rises at a uniform speed for a further time before being brought to rest with a retardation of $4\,\text{m/s}^2$. Find the force in the hoisting cable when: (a) the lift is accelerating, (b) when the lift is moving with uniform speed, and (c) when the lift is decelerating. The weight of the lift is 5 kN.

SOLUTION

Let T be the force in the hoisting cable.

(a)   When the lift is accelerating upwards T must be greater than W, the weight of the lift (Fig. 10.1). Hence the resultant force causing acceleration is $T-W$. From equation [10.1]

$$T-W = ma$$

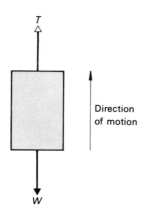

Fig. 10.1   The solution to Worked Example 3

From equation [10.2]

$$m = \frac{W}{9.81} = \frac{5000}{9.81} = 510 \text{ kg}$$

$$T - 5000 = 510 \times 3$$

$$T = 5000 + 1530 = 6530 \text{ N} = 6.53 \text{ kN}$$

Hence when the lift is accelerating upwards the force in the hoisting cable is 6.53 kN.

(b) When the lift is moving with uniform speed the force in the hoisting cable is equal to the weight of the lift, i.e. it is 5 kN.

(c) When the lift is retarding the acceleration may be regarded as being negative. Hence

$$T - 5000 = -510 \times 4$$

$$T - 5000 = -2040$$

Therefore $T = 2960 \text{ N} = 2.96 \text{ kN}$

Hence when the lift is retarding the force in the hoisting cable is only 2.96 kN.

EXERCISE 10 _____

1) A body of mass 50 kg is free to move. If a force of 5 newtons is applied what will be the acceleration given to the body?

2) The force causing an iron core to move in an electric solenoid is 2 N and the mass of the core is 300 grams. With what acceleration will it move?

3) A body having a mass of 20 kg falls freely from rest near to the earth's surface. (a) What will be the gravitational force on the body? (Assume $g = 9.81 \text{ m/s}^2$.) (b) How far will the body fall during a period of 5 seconds? Give your answers to four significant figures.

4) A body which is free to move is given an acceleration of 72 m/s². Because of this acceleration and the mass of the body its inertia reaction amounts to 3600 N. Calculate the mass of the body.

5) A hoist and its load have a total weight of 4 kN. They are lifted vertically reaching a velocity of 6 m/s after rising 15 m from rest. Assuming that the acceleration is uniform, calculate the net upward force causing acceleration.

6) A body having a mass of 2.5 kg is moving with a velocity of 4 m/s. A uniform force acts on it and causes its velocity to increase to 12 m/s in 4 s. Calculate the magnitude of the force.

7)   A load of 3 kN is raised by a chain and given a starting acceleration of 0.5 m/s². Determine the total initial pull in the chain.

8)   A lorry weighing 20 000 N is moving at 50 km/h. It is brought to rest in a distance of 28 m. Find the average braking force exerted.

9)   A man weighing 560 N stands in a lift which moves with a uniform acceleration of 4 m/s². Find the reaction between the man and the floor of the lift when the lift is: (a) ascending, (b) descending.

10)   A lift cage weighing 30 kN is suspended from a wire rope. Determine the motion of the cage when the tension in the rope is: (a) 28 kN, (b) 30 kN, and (c) 32 kN. Assume that the cage is ascending.

11   FRICTION

After reaching the end of this chapter you should be able to:

1. *State the simple laws of friction.*
2. *Distinguish between 'static' and 'dynamic' friction.*
3. *Solve problems involving static and dynamic frictior*
4. *Carry out an experimental investigation of a problem .*

FRICTIONAL RESISTANCE

Although a machined surface may look smooth a powerful ᵾ.
reveals that it contains small hollows, raised areas and sharply pointed ₊
which are created by the machining process. When two machined surfaceᵴ
are placed together contact only occurs between the 'high' parts of their
surfaces (Fig. 11.1). The contact area is very small when compared with the
total plan area of the surfaces, and hence very large pressures occur even
when the force holding the surfaces together is quite small. These large
pressures cause the two surfaces to be cold welded together at the points of
contact.

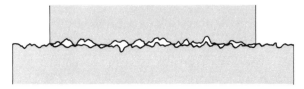

Fig. 11.1   Contact occurs between the 'high' parts of the surfaces

Thus, when an attempt is made to slide one surface over the other, a
resistance to movement occurs which is called *friction*. The force it produces
to prevent or restrict movement is called the *friction force* or the *frictional
resistance* and since it acts to prevent sliding between the surfaces it acts
along the surfaces in contact (Fig. 11.2).

When an external force is applied which tends to cause sliding between the
surfaces the friction force acts as a reaction to the external force. It alters
as the external force alters and remains equal to the external force until
sliding takes place which can only occur when the external force is great
enough to shear the cold welds. Thus the maximum value of the friction
force occurs just before sliding takes place.

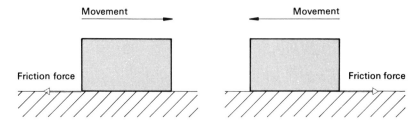

Fig. 11.2   The friction force acts to prevent sliding

THE COEFFICIENT OF FRICTION

Fig. 11.3 shows a block A being pressed against a block B by means of a force Q acting at right angles (i.e. normal) to the surfaces in contact. Block B reacts with an equal and opposite force N.

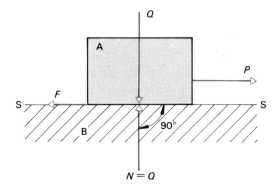

Fig. 11.3   The forces acting on two blocks in contact

Let an external force P be applied to A acting parallel to the common surface of the two blocks and just large enough to cause A to slide with uniform speed over block B. If F is the friction force, then F will be equal and opposite to P and it will act horizontally along the common surface of the two blocks. A force which acts along a surface is said to be tangential to that surface, and hence F is a tangential force.

Experiments carried out on pairs of bodies such as the blocks A and B show that the fraction P/N has a value which is approximately constant for any two materials in contact. That is,

$$\frac{P}{N} = \text{A constant}$$

This constant is represented by the Greek letter μ (mu), so that

$$\frac{P}{N} = \mu \qquad\qquad [11.1]$$

or $\qquad\qquad\qquad\qquad P = \mu N \qquad\qquad [11.2]$

Because $F = P$, then also

$$F = \mu N \qquad\qquad [11.3]$$

where μ is called the coefficient of friction. It has no units since both F and N are in newtons.

WORKED EXAMPLE 1

In an experiment a block of steel of weight 100 N is supported on a horizontal cast iron surface. It was found that a force of 40 N was required to move the block at uniform speed over the cast iron surface. Find the coefficient of friction of steel on cast iron.

SOLUTION

The force pressing the surfaces together is the weight of the block and hence $N = 100$ N and we are given that $P = 40$ N. Using equation [11.1] we have

$$\mu = \frac{P}{N} = \frac{40}{100} = 0.4$$

STATIC AND DYNAMIC FRICTION _____

The maximum resistance to the sliding of one surface over another is often called the *static frictional resistance* because up to the point of sliding the surfaces remain at rest relative to each other.

Friction causes heat to be generated, but when two parts move slowly over one another not much heat is generated and the frictional resistance remains approximately equal to its static value. As the velocity of sliding increases more heat is generated and this causes a reduction in the shear strength of the cold welds. Hence the value of μ is reduced somewhat. Fig. 11.4 shows the relationship between the sliding velocity and the corresponding value of the dynamic coefficient of friction μ_k.

At even higher sliding velocities the value of μ_k becomes constant. However, the value of μ_k will often be taken to be the same as the static values.

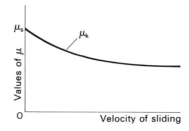

Fig. 11.4   The relationship between sliding velocity and the dynamic coefficient of friction

WORKED EXAMPLE 2

A planing machine and its table are both made of cast iron. If the table weighs 1600 N and the coefficient of friction between the machine and the table is 0.2, calculate the force required to move the table with uniform speed along the horizontal bed of the machine.

SOLUTION

Using equation [11.2], the required force is

$$P = \mu N$$

where $N = 1600$ N, the reaction of the bed to the weight of the table.

$$P = 0.2 \times 1600 = 320 \text{ N}$$

THE LAWS OF FRICTION _____

If the velocity of sliding and the loading forces are not high then the frictional resistance is:

(a)   directly proportional to the normal reaction between the surfaces;

(b)   affected by nature of the surfaces, i.e. the materials used and the degree of roughness;

(c)   independent of the surface area in contact;

(d)   almost independent of the velocity of sliding.

These statements are known as the laws of friction. They relate only to clean dry surfaces and need modification when the condition of the surfaces is otherwise.

WORKED EXAMPLE 3

A casting weighing 500 N is moved with a steady speed over a horizontal floor by a force of $P = 100$ N acting at 30° to the horizontal as shown in Fig. 11.5. Find the value of the coefficient of friction between the casting and the floor.

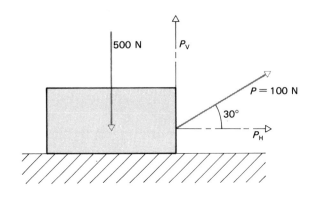

Fig. 11.5   Information for Worked Example 3

SOLUTION

Splitting the force of 100 N into its horizontal and vertical components, we have

$$P_H = 100 \cos 30° = 87 \text{ N}$$
$$P_V = 100 \sin 30° = 50 \text{ N}$$

The normal reaction of the floor is then

$$N = \text{Weight of casting} - P_V$$
$$= 500 - 50 = 450 \text{ N}$$

The force causing sliding is

$$P_H = 87 \text{ N}$$

Using equation [11.2] gives

$$\mu_k = \frac{P_H}{N} = \frac{87}{450} = 0.19$$

WORKED EXAMPLE 4

The load on a bearing which supports a horizontal shaft is 3000 N and the shaft has a diameter of 250 mm (Fig. 11.6). If the coefficient of friction between the shaft and the bearing is 0.02, calculate the turning moment which must be applied to the shaft to overcome the frictional resistance of the bearing.

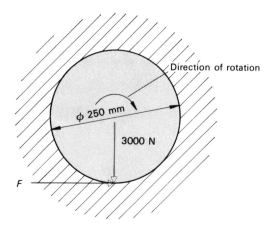

Fig. 11.6   Information for Worked Example 4

SOLUTION

The normal reaction at the bearing is equal to the load on the bearing, i.e.

$$N = 3000\,N$$

From equation [11.3] the friction force is

$$F = \mu N = 0.02 \times 3000 = 60\,N$$

The required turning moment is

$$M = \text{Frictional resistance} \times \text{Radius}$$
$$= 60 \times 0.125 = 7.5\,N\,m$$

(Note that the shaft radius is 125 mm = 0.125 m.)

WORKED EXAMPLE 5

During an experiment to determine the coefficient of friction for brake lining, a metal block is loaded as shown in the table below. The block is then pulled over a horizontal surface on to which the brake lining has been fixed at a steady speed. The force needed is then recorded.

Normal reaction between surfaces (N newtons)	5	15	27.5	35	45	50
Force needed to overcome friction (P newtons)	2.0	6.1	11.0	13.9	18.1	20.0

Draw a graph of P against N taking values of P on the vertical axis, and hence determine the value of the coefficient of friction.

SOLUTION

The graph is shown in Fig. 11.7. The points are seen to deviate only slightly from a straight line. Since the figures are the result of an experiment, errors in measurement must be expected and hence the best straight line is drawn through the points. Since $\mu = \dfrac{P}{N}$, the gradient of the line gives the value of the coefficient of friction. By drawing the right-angled triangle ABC,

$$\text{Gradient} = \frac{BC}{AC} = \frac{12}{30} = 0.4$$

Hence the value of the coefficient of friction is 0.4.

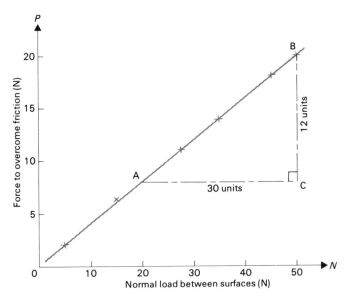

Fig. 11.7   The solution to Worked Example 5

EXERCISE 11

1) A block of cast iron is drawn slowly along a horizontal table. If the coefficient of friction between the surfaces is 0.4 and the block weighs 40 N, calculate the force required to move the block.

2) A force of 11 N will just move a block of wood weighing 33 N along a horizontal surface. Calculate the value of the coefficient of friction.

3) A casting weighing 4000 N is to be pulled across a horizontal floor. If the coefficient of friction between the floor and the casting is 0.25, find the horizontal pull that would be necessary to pull the casting across the floor at a steady speed.

4) A metal box weighing 200 N is pulled across a level surface at uniform speed by a horizontal pull of 65 N. An additional weight of 80 N is now added to the box. Calculate the force now needed to move the box at uniform speed. If the maximum horizontal pull that can be applied is 100 N, what is the greatest weight that can be added to the box?

5)   A body having a weight of 40 N lies on a horizontal surface. A force of 12 N applied at 45° to the horizontal will just move the weight. Calculate the value of the coefficient of friction.

6)   A casting weighing 2400 N is pulled along a horizontal floor by a chain which makes an angle of 30° with the horizontal. If a force in the chain of 250 N is required to move the casting at a steady speed, determine the value of the coefficient of friction between the floor and the casting.

7)   During an experiment to determine the value of the coefficient of friction between two sliding surfaces the following results were obtained:

Normal load between surfaces (N newtons)	4	12	21	28	36	40
Force to overcome friction (P newtons)	1.6	4.9	8.8	11.1	14.5	16.0

Plot a graph of P against N taking values of P on the vertical axis. Hence determine the value of the coefficient of friction.

8)   A brake drum 1.4 m diameter rotates at a steady speed. The brake block is lined with fabric whose coefficient of friction is 0.4. If the normal force between the block and the drum is 800 N, calculate the turning moment which will bring the drum to rest.

9)   A pulley has a diameter of 300 mm and it is mounted on a horizontal shaft carried in plain bearings having a diameter of 50 mm. If the load on each bearing is 100 N and the static and dynamic coefficients of friction are 0.15 and 0.12 respectively, calculate the tangential force which must be applied to the rim of the pulley: (a) to start the pulley rotating, (b) to maintain motion once it has begun.

10)   When dry the coefficient of friction between two metal plates in contact is 0.35 and the tangential force required to cause sliding is 70 N. If the plates are immersed in oil so that the coefficient of friction is reduced to 0.07, calculate the necessary increase in the normal force between the plates if the tangential force to cause sliding remains constant at 70 N.

12

ENERGY

After reaching the end of this chapter you should be able to:

1. Calculate the energy transferred by a constant force acting over a distance, i.e. work.
2. Describe potential energy as energy due to the position of a body and derive the expression p.e. = mgh.
3. Describe kinetic energy as the energy due to the motion of a body and derive the relationship k.e. = $\frac{1}{2}mv^2$.
4. State the law of the conservation of energy.
5. Calculate potential and kinetic energies and solve problems where mechanical energy is considered to be conserved.
6. Calculate the energy transferred when a temperature change or a change of state occurs, i.e. calculations involving specific heat capacity and specific latent heat.

WORK

Work is done when a force produces motion. It is calculated from:

> Work done = Force on the body measured in the direction of motion
> × Distance moved by the body

[12.1]

In the case of a torque:

> Work done = Torque × Angle turned through (in radians)   [12.2]

where

Torque = Force × Perpendicular distance from the line of action of the
force to the axis about which the torque is applied

In SI the unit of work is the joule (J) which is defined as the work done when a force of 1 newton moves its point of application through a distance of 1 metre. That is,

> 1 joule = 1 newton metre

WORKED EXAMPLE 1

A truck requires a horizontal force of 500 N to move it along a horizontal track at constant speed. How much work is done in moving it 300 m along the track?

SOLUTION

$$\text{Work done} = \text{Force} \times \text{Distance}$$
$$= 500 \times 300 = 150\,000\,\text{J} = 150\,\text{kJ}$$

WORKED EXAMPLE 2

A box is pulled along a horizontal floor at constant speed by a rope inclined upwards from the floor at an angle of 30°. If the tension in the rope is 200 N, find the work done in moving the box a distance of 8 metres.

SOLUTION

From Fig. 12.1 it can be seen that the component of the tension in the rope in the direction of motion is $200\cos 30°$. Hence

$$\text{Work done} = 200\cos 30° \times 8 = 1386\,\text{J} = 1.386\,\text{kJ}$$

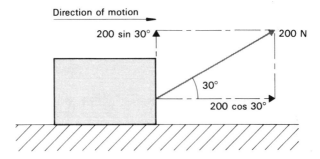

Fig. 12.1   Information for the solution to Worked Example 2

WORKED EXAMPLE 3

A rotor having a mass of 50 kg is lifted by a crane through a height of 12 m at constant speed. Calculate the work done.

SOLUTION

$$\text{Force exerted by the crane} = \text{Weight of the rotor}$$
$$= 50 \times 9.81 = 490.5\,\text{N}$$
$$\text{Work done} = \text{Force} \times \text{Distance}$$
$$= 490.5 \times 8 = 3924\,\text{J} = 3.924\,\text{kJ}$$

WORKED EXAMPLE 4

In order to turn a shaft a belt passes over a pulley whose diameter is 750 mm. If the effective pull in the belt is 2600 N, find the work done if the shaft makes 20 revolutions.

SOLUTION

$$\text{Torque} = 2600 \times 0.375 = 975 \, \text{N m}$$
$$\text{Angle turned through} = 2\pi \times 20 = 125.7 \, \text{radians}$$
$$\text{Work done} = \text{Torque} \times \text{Angle turned through}$$
$$= 975 \times 125.7 = 122\,600 \, \text{J} = 122.6 \, \text{kJ}$$

GRAPHICAL REPRESENTATION OF WORK DONE _____

When work is done by a force it can be represented by the area under a force–distance graph. Similarly, when work is done by a torque it can be represented by the area under a torque–angle turned through graph.

WORKED EXAMPLE 5

A constant force of 5000 N is required to move a machine a distance of 25 m across a workshop floor. Represent this information on a force–distance graph and hence calculate the work done.

SOLUTION

The force–distance graph is shown in Fig. 12.2. The work done is given by the area under the graph (shown shaded) and hence

$$\text{Work done} = 5000 \times 25 = 125\,000 \, \text{J} = 125 \, \text{kJ}$$

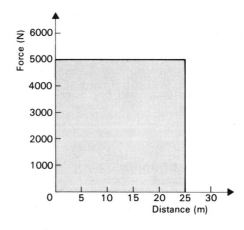

Fig. 12.2   Work done = Area under a force–distance graph

WORKED EXAMPLE 6

A braking force brings a moving body to rest in a distance of 10 m. During the first 4 m the force rises uniformly from 600 N to 1800 N and then remains constant at 1800 N during the next 3 m of movement after which it falls uniformly to zero in the remaining 3 m. Draw a force–distance graph representing the way the force changes with distance and determine the work done in bringing the body to rest.

SOLUTION

The force–distance graph is drawn in Fig. 12.3, and the work done is represented by the area ABCDE.

$$\begin{aligned}
\text{Work done} &= \text{Area BCH} + \text{Area ABHG} + \text{Area GCDF} + \text{Area FDE} \\
&= (\tfrac{1}{2} \times 1200 \times 4) + (600 \times 4) + (1800 \times 3) + (\tfrac{1}{2} \times 1800 \times 3) \\
&= 2400 + 2400 + 5400 + 2700 \\
&= 12\,900\,\text{J} = 12.9\,\text{kJ}
\end{aligned}$$

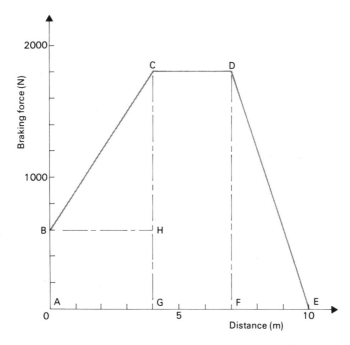

Fig. 12.3   The force–distance graph for Worked Example 6

WORKED EXAMPLE 7

In order to turn a shaft through one complete revolution a force is applied tangentially to the rim of a pulley which is keyed to the shaft. The pulley diameter is 0.5 m. During rotation the force varies as follows: starting at zero it rises uniformly to 160 N during the first third of a revolution. It then remains constant at 160 N during the next quarter of the revolution and finally falls uniformly to zero during the remainder of the revolution. Draw a torque–angle turned through graph and hence calculate the work done during the revolution.

SOLUTION

The torque is found by multiplying the force by the pulley radius so that

When the force is zero: Torque $= 0 \times 0.25 = 0\,\text{N m}$

When the force is 160 N: Torque $= 160 \times 0.25 = 40\,\text{N m}$

Now $\dfrac{1}{3}$ of a revolution $= \dfrac{2\pi}{3} = \dfrac{4}{6}\pi$ radians

$\dfrac{1}{4}$ of a revolution $= \dfrac{2\pi}{4} = \dfrac{3}{6}\pi$ radians

$\dfrac{5}{12}$ of a revolution $= \dfrac{5}{12} \times 2\pi = \dfrac{5}{6}\pi$ radians

The torque–angle turned through graph can now be drawn as shown in Fig. 12.4.

Work done in 1 revolution $=$ Area ABCD

$=$ Area ABE + Area EBCF + Area FCD

$= (\tfrac{1}{2} \times 40 \times \tfrac{4}{6}\pi) + (40 \times \tfrac{3}{6}\pi) + (\tfrac{1}{2} \times 40 \times \tfrac{5}{6}\pi)$

$= 41.87 + 62.8 + 52.33$

$= 157\,\text{J}$

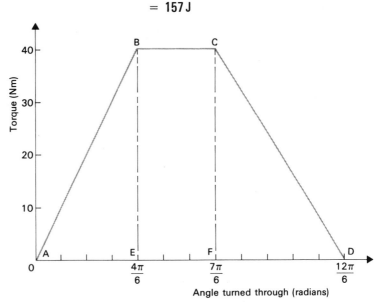

Fig. 12.4   The torque–angle turned through graph for Worked Example 7

ENERGY

Energy is the ability to do work and hence it is measured in the same units as those of work, that is, in joules. Energy exists in various forms which include two very important kinds of mechanical energy: *potential energy* and *kinetic energy*.

POTENTIAL ENERGY

Potential energy is the energy possessed by a body by virtue of its position above a datum such as the surface of the earth, a workshop floor or the top of a bench.

Fig. 12.5 shows a mass of m kilograms which has been raised through a height of h metres above a datum A–A. The force F required to raise the mass must equal the gravitational pull on the mass, that is, it must equal the weight of the mass. Hence

$$\text{Work done on the mass} = \text{Force} \times \text{Height lifted}$$
$$= mgh$$

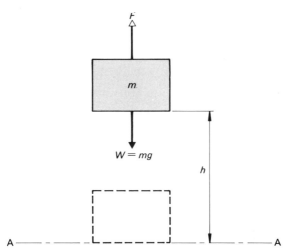

Fig. 12.5   Potential energy is energy possessed by a body by virtue of its position above a datum

The potential energy stored in the body is equal to the work done in raising it through the height h metres, and therefore

$$\text{Potential energy with respect to datum A–A} = mgh \qquad [12.3]$$

KINETIC ENERGY

Kinetic energy is the energy possessed by a body by virtue of its motion.

Consider a body of mass m moving with a velocity of v. Suppose that the body starts from rest and is acted upon by a force F and that no friction or other forces act on the body.

This force F will give the body a uniform acceleration a, and it will acquire a final velocity v after travelling a distance s.

The quantities a, v and s are connected by the equation

$$v^2 = u^2 + 2as$$

The work done by the force F in moving the body through the distance s is converted into kinetic energy in the body. Thus

$$\text{Work done} = \text{Force} \times \text{Distance} = Fs$$

but
$$F = ma$$

$$\text{Work done} = mas$$

Using the equation $v^2 = u^2 + 2as$ and remembering that $u = 0$ gives

$$a = \frac{v^2}{2s}$$

$$\text{Work done} = m \times \frac{v^2}{2s} \times s = \tfrac{1}{2}mv^2$$

$$\boxed{\text{Kinetic energy} = \tfrac{1}{2}mv^2}$$ [12.4]

WORKED EXAMPLE 8

A truck has a mass of 3 tonnes. If it is moving at 45 km/h, how much kinetic energy does it possess?

SOLUTION

We have

$$m = 3 \text{ tonnes} = 3000 \text{ kg}$$

$$v = 45 \text{ km/h} = \frac{45 \times 1000}{60 \times 60} = 12.5 \text{ m/s}$$

$$\text{Kinetic energy possessed by the truck} = \tfrac{1}{2}mv^2$$
$$= \tfrac{1}{2} \times 3000 \times 12.5^2$$
$$= 234\,000 \text{ J} = 234 \text{ kJ}$$

THE PRINCIPLE OF THE CONSERVATION OF ENERGY _____

Fig. 12.6 shows a body of mass m positioned at a height h above a datum A–A. If it is allowed to fall it reaches its maximum velocity just as it arrives at the datum A–A. That is, the body attains its maximum kinetic energy when its potential energy is zero. Thus

$$\boxed{\text{Loss in potential energy} = \text{Gain in kinetic energy}}$$ [12.5]

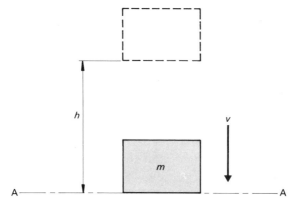

Fig. 12.6   A body falling from a height loses potential energy but gains kinetic energy

This important statement is a special case of the principle of the conservation of energy which states that energy can neither be created nor destroyed but can only be changed in form.

WORKED EXAMPLE 9

A steel ball having a mass of 100 grams falls from a height of 1.8 m on to a plate and rebounds to a height of 1.25 m. Determine: (a) the potential energy of the ball before the fall; (b) the kinetic energy possessed by the ball as it hits the plate; (c) the velocity of the ball as it hits the plate; (d) the kinetic energy of the ball as it leaves the plate on the rebound; (e) the velocity of the ball on rebound.

SOLUTION

(a)   From equation [12.3]

$$\text{Potential energy} = mgh = 0.1 \times 9.81 \times 1.8 = 1.77 \text{ J}$$

(b)   Using the law of the conservation of energy (equation [12.5]) gives

$$\text{Kinetic energy} = \text{Loss of potential energy} = 1.77 \text{ J}$$

(c)   From equation [12.4]

$$\tfrac{1}{2}mv^2 = 1.77$$

$$v = \sqrt{\frac{2 \times 1.77}{m}} = \sqrt{\frac{2 \times 1.77}{0.1}} = 5.95 \text{ m/s}$$

(d)   Again using the law of the conservation of energy, for this stage in which the ball rises after rebound gives

$$\text{Loss of kinetic energy} = \text{Gain in potential energy}$$

$$\text{Kinetic energy at rebound} = mgh$$

$$= 0.1 \times 9.81 \times 1.25$$

$$= 1.23 \text{ J}$$

The kinetic energy lost has been used in distorting the plate.

(e)

$$\tfrac{1}{2}mv^2 = mgh$$

$$v = \sqrt{2gh} = \sqrt{2 \times 9.81 \times 1.25} = 4.95\,\text{m/s}$$

HEAT TRANSFER

All substances consist of *atoms* or *molecules*. These atoms and molecules are in continuous motion and hence each molecule contains a store of kinetic energy. When a body is heated the atoms and molecules move more quickly and hence a heated body possesses a greater store of energy than a cold body. The energy possessed by a body as a result of its temperature is called *internal energy*.

When two bodies at different temperatures are placed in contact with each other, some of the internal energy possessed by the hotter body is transferred to the colder body. This happens because the quickly moving molecules of the hot body collide with the slower moving molecules of the colder body so increasing their speed. The kinetic energy of the molecules in the colder body is thereby increased thus increasing the amount of heat energy possessed by the colder body. At the same time the molecules in the hotter body lose kinetic energy because the collisions slow them down and hence the hotter body loses internal energy.

The passage of internal energy from one body to another is called heat transfer and the energy being transferred is called heat energy.

CHANGE OF STATE

Matter can exist in any one of three forms depending upon whether the molecules of the substance are:

(a)   held closely together able only to vibrate about fixed positions (*solids*);

(b)   can move easily over each other but are prevented by intermolecular forces from separating completely (*liquids*);

(c)   are free to move at random, colliding but never, by reason of their high velocities, remaining together (*gases*).

The particular state that a substance is in will depend upon the energy of its molecules. It follows, therefore, that if a body is to change from a solid to a liquid or a liquid to a gas, there must be a transfer of heat energy *to* the body, or *from* the body if the process is to be reversed.

TERMINOLOGY

When a solid substance receives heat energy it will increase in temperature until a certain point is reached and at that temperature a change of state occurs and the solid becomes a liquid. In short, the solid *melts* and the temperature at which this occurs is called the *melting point* of the substance.

The input of additional heat energy will now further raise the temperature of the liquid until the *boiling point* is reached when, if boiling continues, the liquid is transformed into a *vapour* and the liquid is said to have been *vaporised.*

Vapours resemble gases, but near to their point of liquefaction they behave somewhat differently from true gases when subjected to changes of temperature, pressure and volume. This is particularly appropriate to steam formed above boiling water as opposed to steam which is far removed in temperature from its boiling point by being further heated or *superheated*.

If a vapour is cooled, at some temperature it liquefies. This temperature is the *temperature of liquefaction*. Further cooling lowers the temperature until the liquid begins to solidify or freeze, i.e. become solid. This temperature is known as the *freezing point* of the substance.

Thus the words 'melt' and 'boil' and 'vaporise' refer to changes of state which occur as energy is given to the substance whereas 'liquefy' and 'solidify' refer to changes of state which occur as energy is removed from the substance. In general, for any one substance, melting or freezing will occur at one particular temperature and vaporisation or liquefaction at some other particular temperature.

THE TWO EFFECTS OF HEAT TRANSFER

As heat is continuously given to a substance, its temperature rises unless it is undergoing a change of state (Fig. 12.7). The transfer of heat energy to or from a body can therefore cause either:

(a)   a change of temperature without a change of state, or

(b)   a change of state without a change of temperature.

These two quite separate effects involve two quite separate notions, namely *specific heat capacity* and *specific latent heat* respectively.

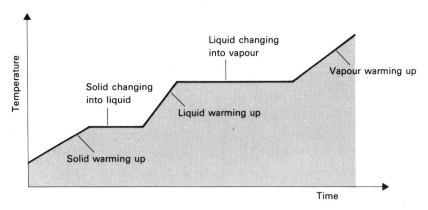

Fig. 12.7   Change of state

SPECIFIC HEAT CAPACITY

The change in temperature of a heated substance depends solely on two factors: the substance being heated and how much of it is being heated (i.e. the mass of substance being heated).

For any one substance the energy required to raise unit mass (1 kg) of the substance through a unit rise in temperature (1°C) is constant. This quantity of heat is called the specific heat capacity (c) for that substance over normal temperature ranges so that

Heat energy given to body = Mass of body × Specific heat capacity
                                            × Temperature rise

or

$$\Delta Q = mc\Delta\theta$$ [12.6]

WORKED EXAMPLE 10

The specific heat capacity of mild steel is 0.486 kJ/kg °C. Calculate the heat energy needed to raise the temperature of a 20 kg mild steel forging from 15 °C to 500 °C.

SOLUTION

$$\text{Temperature rise } \Delta\theta = 500 - 15 = 485\,°C$$
$$\text{Mass of the forging } m = 20\,\text{kg}$$
$$\text{Specific heat capacity } c = 0.486\,\text{kJ/kg}\,°C$$

Then,

$$\text{Required heat transfer } \Delta Q = 20 \times 0.486 \times 485$$
$$= 4714.2\,\text{kJ}$$

Specific heat capacities must be obtained experimentally. Approximate values of c for some common substances are given in Table 12.1.

TABLE 12.1

Substance	Specific heat capacity (J/kg °C)
Metals	
Aluminium	946
Copper	385
Gold	129
Iron	476
Lead	124
Magnesium	1043
Mercury	139
Silver	237
Steel	480
Tungsten	142
Non-metallic solids	
Asbestos	1047
Carbon, graphite	528
Diamond	615
Chalk	895
Glass	832
Granite	837
Silicon	758
Ice	2090
Liquids	
Water	4180
Glycerine	2408
Olive Oil	1969
Petrol	2090
Turpentine	1718

SPECIFIC LATENT HEAT

If the transfer of heat to a substance is continued, eventually its melting point (if a solid) or boiling point (if a liquid) is reached. Individual molecules with kinetic energies a little above the average cannot be held in place, and they begin to move more freely either as a liquid or a gas. So a change of state begins to take place throughout the substance. As the faster molecules break away the *average* molecular energy (temperature) of the remaining ones would be reduced if it were not for the supply of further heat energy. As energy is continuously supplied the temperature at which the substance melts (or boils) is maintained but cannot be exceeded, since the additional energy is used up in completing the change. The change of state continues at a rate which depends upon the rate at which energy is supplied.

The heat energy supplied during a change of state does not therefore result in a change in temperature and is not, therefore, apparent to the sense of touch. Because of this the heat energy transferred to a body to cause a change of state is called *latent* (i.e. hidden, undeveloped) *heat.*

The amount of latent heat required to change the state of a given mass of a substance at a given pressure depends upon (a) the substance and (b) whether the change of state is from a solid to a liquid or, a liquid to a vapour or gas. Hence each substance has:

(a) *a specific latent heat of fusion*, which is the amount of heat energy required to change 1 kg of the substance from the solid to the liquid form at constant temperature and pressure;

(b) *a specific latent heat of vaporisation*, which is the amount of heat energy required to change 1 kg of the substance from the liquid to the vapour state at constant temperature and pressure.

MEASUREMENT OF LATENT HEAT

The specific latent heat of fusion or vaporisation of a substance is denoted by the symbol L, so that, if ΔQ of heat is given to a mass m as the change of state is taking place, then

$$\Delta Q = mL \qquad [12.7]$$

Changes of state are reversible. A vapour will liquefy and a liquid solidify if heat energy is taken from the body. In such cases equation [12.7] expresses the heat energy given up by the body as it liquefies or solidifies.

Table 12.2 gives the melting and boiling points of some common substances together with their approximate latent heats of fusion and vaporisation at atmospheric pressure.

TABLE 12.2

Substance	Melting or freezing point (°C)	Boiling point (°C)	Specific latent heat of fusion (kJ/kg)	Specific latent heat of vaporisation (kJ/kg)
Aluminium	660	2056	396	8374
Copper	1083	2580	212	7352
Gold	1063	2966	67	1867
Iron	1535	2988	272	4647
Lead	327	1750	26	1352
Magnesium	650	1107	272	6200
Mercury	−38.9	357	12	297
Nickel	1452	2800	309	4228
Silver	961	2001	102	2310
Tin	232	2600	59	2742
Tungsten	3370	5927	184	4953
Ammonia	−75	−33	452	1370
Ether	−	38	−	379
Glycerine	18	290	199	−
Turpentine	−10	160	−	290
Ice/water	0	100	335	2257

WORKED EXAMPLE 11

Calculate the heat energy required to convert 52 kg of water at 100 °C and atmospheric pressure into steam at the same temperature and pressure. The specific latent heat of vaporisation of water at atmospheric pressure is 2257 kJ/kg.

SOLUTION

$$Required\ heat\ energy\ \Delta Q = mL$$
$$= 52 \times 2257$$
$$= 117\ 364\ kJ$$

WORKED EXAMPLE 12

What amount of heat energy will be necessary to melt 15 kg of aluminium? The specific latent heat of fusion of aluminium is 396 kJ/kg.

SOLUTION

$$Required\ heat\ energy\ \Delta Q = mL$$
$$= 15 \times 396$$
$$= 5940\ kJ$$

WORKED EXAMPLE 13

Determine the amount of heat required to convert 1 kg of ice at $-12\,^\circ$C to steam at 100 $^\circ$C.

Specific heat capacity of ice = 2090 J/kg $^\circ$C.

Specific heat capacity of water = 4180 J/kg $^\circ$C.

Specific latent heat of fusion of ice at 0 $^\circ$C = 335 kJ/kg.

Specific latent heat of vaporisation of water at 100 $^\circ$C = 2257 kJ/kg.

Plot a graph relating the change in temperature with the heat energy required.

SOLUTION

(i)   Heat energy to raise the temperature of the ice from $-12\,^\circ$C to 0 $^\circ$C:

$$\Delta Q_1 = m\theta c$$
$$= 1 \times 12 \times 2090$$
$$= 25\,080\,\text{J}$$
$$= 25.08\,\text{kJ}$$

(ii)   Heat energy to convert the ice at 0 $^\circ$C to water at 0 $^\circ$C:

$$\Delta Q_2 = mL$$
$$= 1 \times 335$$
$$= 335\,\text{kJ}$$

(iii) Heat energy to raise the temperature of the water from 0 $^\circ$C to 100 $^\circ$C:

$$\Delta Q_3 = mc\Delta\theta$$
$$= 1 \times 100 \times 4180$$
$$= 418\,000\,\text{J}$$
$$= 418\,\text{kJ}$$

(iv)   Heat energy to convert the mass of water at 100 $^\circ$C into steam at 100 $^\circ$C:

$$\Delta Q_4 = mL$$
$$= 1 \times 2257$$
$$= 2257\,\text{kJ}$$

Therefore

$$\text{Total heat required} = 25.08 + 335 + 418 + 2257$$
$$= 3035.08\,\text{kJ}$$

Fig. 12.8 shows the graph relating temperature change with the required heat energy/input.

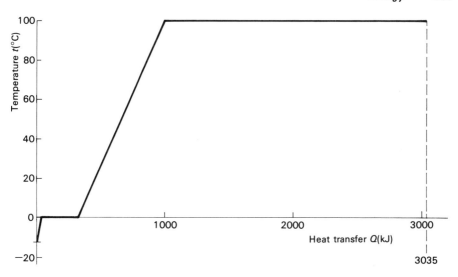

Fig. 12.8   Graph for Worked Example 13

WORKED EXAMPLE 14

Five kilograms of lead shot are cooled from a temperature of 270 °C by allowing the mass to fall into 50 litres of water initially at a temperature of 15 °C. Assuming that the heat transfer is entirely between the lead shot and the water and that there are no heat losses, calculate the final temperature of the water and shot. The specific heat capacities of lead and water are 124 and 4180 J/kg°C respectively. One litre of water has a mass of 1 kilogram.

SOLUTION

The total mass of water will be 50 kilograms. Let

Let θ_1 be the final temperature of the water and the shot. Then

$$\text{Heat lost by lead shot} = \text{Heat gained by the water}$$

i.e.

$$\begin{pmatrix}\text{Mass of lead} \times \text{Sp. heat capacity of lead} \\ \times \text{Temperature fall}\end{pmatrix} = \begin{pmatrix}\text{Mass of water} \times \text{Sp. heat capacity of water} \\ \times \text{Temperature rise}\end{pmatrix}$$

$$5 \times 124 \times (270 - \theta_1) = 50 \times 4180 \times (\theta_1 - 15)$$

$$167\,400 - 620\theta_1 = 209\,000\theta_1 - 3\,135\,000$$

$$209\,000\theta_1 + 620\theta_1 = 3\,135\,000 + 167\,400$$

$$209\,620\theta_1 = 3\,302\,400$$

$$\theta_1 = 15.75°C$$

EXERCISE 12 _____

(Take $g = 9.81\,\text{m/s}^2$.)

1) How much work is done when a mass of 6 kg is lifted, at constant speed, through a height of 12 m?

2) A mass of 330 kg is lifted at constant speed by a crane through a height of 15 m. Calculate the amount of work done.

3) A force of 120 N is required to move a trolley at constant speed along a level track. How much work is done in moving the trolley 20 m along the track?

4) A shaping machine is cutting a surface 150 mm long by 100 mm wide. The cutting force is 600 N and on each stroke the job moves across 4 mm. Determine the work done in traversing the full width of the surface.

5) A box is moved a distance of 8 m along a horizontal floor at constant speed by the action of a force of 40 N whose inclination is $20°$ above the horizontal. Calculate the work done by the force.

6) The force required to move a body over a specified distance is related to distance as follows:

      0–6 m   a constant force of 220 N

      6–20 m   a uniformly increasing force from 220 N to 400 N

      20–40 m   a uniformly decreasing force from 400 N to 220 N

Draw a force–distance graph and find the work done by the force.

7) The force acting on a body varies uniformly from 0 to 200 N whilst it moves 2 m. The force then remains constant at 200 N whilst the body moves a further 3 m and then decreases uniformly to zero over a final distance of 2 m. Draw a force–distance graph, and from it calculate the amount of work done by the force.

8) A broach has a stroke of 0.9 m. The resistance offered by the work-piece varies as follows: for the first 0.6 m of the stroke the resistance varies uniformly from 1200 N to 2000 N. For the final 0.3 m the resistance is constant at 2000 N. Calculate the work done during the stroke.

9) The tangential force exerted by a lathe tool when turning work 300 mm diameter is 80 N. Calculate the work done when the work makes 25 revolutions.

10)   The saddle of a lathe is moved by a constant force of 30 N which moves in a circle 180 mm diameter. If the handle is turned 20 times, how much work is done?

11)   A truck is pulled along a floor at constant speed by a rope which is inclined upwards at an angle of 25°. If the tension in the rope is 220 N, calculate the work done in moving the truck a distance of 15 m.

12)   In tightening up a nut, the force required at the end of a spanner 150 mm long increases uniformly from zero to 30 N over $\frac{1}{4}$ rev. Calculate the work done in this operation.

13)   In order to turn a shaft a force is applied tangentially to the rim of a pulley which is keyed to the shaft. The pulley diameter is 600 mm. During rotation the force varies from zero to 200 N over the first $\frac{1}{2}$ rev. It then remains constant at 200 N for the next $\frac{1}{4}$ rev and then falls uniformly from 200 N to zero during the final $\frac{1}{4}$ rev. Draw a torque–angle turned through diagram and hence determine the work done during the revolution.

14)   A shaft has a diameter of 200 mm and the friction force resisting motion is 1000 N. Calculate the work done in rotating the shaft through 300 revolutions.

15)   Calculate the kinetic energy of: (a) a truck having a mass of 20 kg travelling at 3 m/s, (b) a bullet with a mass of 2 g travelling at 400 m/s, (c) a car with a mass of 1200 kg travelling at 70 km/h.

16)   A mass of 25 kg is raised through a height of 8 m. What is the gain in potential energy?

17)   A body of mass 5 kg falls from rest and has a kinetic energy of 800 J just before touching the ground. (a) How much potential energy has been converted to kinetic energy? (b) From what height has the mass fallen?

18)   A truck having a mass of 10 tonnes is moving at 40 km/h. How much kinetic energy does it possess? If it freewheels up an incline, what vertical height would it attain before coming to rest, assuming that there is no frictional resistance?

19)   A ball having a mass of 6 kg is dropped from a height of 25 m and rebounds with $\frac{3}{4}$ of its impact velocity. Find the kinetic energy and the velocity of the ball just before striking the ground. Determine the height to which the ball will rise after the first rebound.

20)   A body is projected with a velocity of 16 m/s up the line of greatest slope of a smooth plane inclined at 30° to the horizontal. Calculate the distance travelled before the body comes to momentary rest.

21)   The specific heat capacity of aluminium is 946 J/kg°C. Find the heat energy required to raise the temperature of 30 kg of aluminium from 20°C to 240°C.

22)   How much heat energy is needed to raise the temperature of 15 kg of copper from 15°C to 85°C? (Specific heat capacity of copper is 385 J/kg°C.)

23)   Calculate the heat energy required to convert 8 kg of water at 100°C into steam at the same temperature. Assume that the change of state takes place at atmospheric pressure and that the latent heat of vaporisation of water is 2257 kJ/kg.

24)   Equal quantities of heat energy will raise the temperature of 30 kg of water through 10°C and a piece of steel through 80°C. What is the mass of the steel? (Take the specific heat capacities of water and steel to be 4180 and 480 J/kg°C respectively.)

25)   1419 kJ of heat energy is given to a piece of metal having a mass of 25 kg. If the temperature of the metal is increased from 40°C to 100°C what is the specific heat capacity of the metal?

26)   How much heat energy is required to change 10 kg of ice at 0°C into steam at 100°C at atmospheric pressure? (The specific heat capacity of water is 4180 J/kg°C; the specific latent heat of fusion of ice is 335 kJ/kg and the specific latent heat of vaporisation of water is 2257 kJ/kg.)

27)   12 kg of aluminium initially at a temperature of 15°C is to be melted. If the melting point of aluminium is 660°C and its specific heat capacity is 946 J/kg°C and its specific latent heat of fusion is 396 kJ/kg, calculate the amount of heat energy required.

28)   A large aluminium vat has a mass of 350 kg and holds 1500 kg of water both vat and water being at a temperature of 15°C. Assuming that there is no heat loss, what heat transfer is required to raise the vat and its contents to a temperature of 87°C? (Take the specific heat capacities of aluminium and water to be 946 J/kg°C and 4180 J/kg°C respectively.)

29) A length of copper pipe having a mass of 22 kg and a temperature of 500 °C is cooled by placing it in a trough containing 120 kg of water at a temperature of 15 °C. Assuming that heat transfer takes place only between the copper pipe and the water, and that there are no heat losses and no losses due to evaporation, find the final temperature of the pipe and the water. (Take the specific heat capacities of copper and water to be 385 J/kg°C and 4180 J/kg°C respectively.)

30) During a heat treatment process a steel component having a mass of 18 kg and a temperature of 750°C is quenched by immersing it in 200 kg of oil at 20°C. Assuming that all the heat energy removed from the steel is transferred to the oil, determine the final temperature of the oil and the component. (Assume that the specific heat capacities of the steel and the oil are 480 J/kg°C and 2200 J/kg°C respectively.)

31) With reference to question 30, if the steel component had been quenched in 200 kg of water at 20°C instead of in the oil, what would have been the final temperature of the steel and the water? Assume that all the heat energy removed from the component is transferred to the water and take the specific heat capacity of water to be 4180 J/kg°C.

32) When 5 kg of magnesium were raised in temperature from 20°C to 250°C it was found that the necessary heat transfer to the metal was 1200 kJ. Calculate the specific heat capacity of magnesium.

33) Calculate the total heat transfer necessary to melt 85 kg of ice at 0°C in order to provide 85 kg of water at 0°C. The specific latent heat of fusion of ice is 335 kJ/kg.

34) Calculate the total heat transfer necessary to vaporise 85 kg of water at 100°C and at atmospheric pressure in order to provide 85 kg of steam at 100°C. The specific latent heat of vaporisation of water is 2257 kJ/kg.

35) Ice cubes at a temperature of −5°C are to be made by pouring 1 kg of water at 20°C into a mould and placing it and its contents in a refrigerator which is already at a temperature of −5°C. Calculate the heat transfer from the refrigerator to the surrounding air which will take place during the making of the ice cubes.

Specific heat capacity of water = 4180 J/kg°C.

Specific heat capacity of ice = 2090 J/kg°C.

Specific latent heat of fusion of ice = 335 kJ/kg.

Neglect any losses due to the inefficiency of the refrigerator.

36)   A small electric furnace is used to melt 4 kg of gold held in a crucible. Determine the quantity of heat energy which must be transferred to the gold alone if the initial temperature of the metal is 20°C. Take the melting point of gold to be 1063 °C. The specific heat capacity and specific latent heat of fusion of gold are 129 J/kg°C and 67 kJ/kg respectively.

37)   The nose cone of a space capsule is to be covered with tungsten so that upon re-entry the heat energy created by friction with the atmosphere will be dissipated as the layers of tungsten are first liquefied and then vaporised. If the tungsten has a mass of 2000 kg calculate the total amount of heat energy which will be dissipated assuming that three quarters of this tungsten heat shield is vaporised during re-entry. Assume also that the initial temperature of the tungsten is that of outer space, i.e. −273°C, the melting point 3370°C and the boiling point 5927°C. Take the specific heat capacity of both solid and liquid tungsten to be 142 J/kg°C and the specific latent heat of fusion and vaporisation as 184 and 4953 kJ/kg respectively.

38)   Refer to question 37. The total mass of the capsule will be 3500 kg before re-entry. If the heat transfer represents the kinetic energy that the capsule had just before reaching the earth's atmosphere, calculate the velocity of the capsule at that moment. (*Hint*: The kinetic energy of a mass $m = \frac{1}{2}mv^2$ joules.)

13 EXPANSION

Describe the relationship between temperature and increase of (a) linear dimensions of solids, (b) volumes of liquids.
Define the coefficients of expansion.
Solve simple problems involving changes of temperature and dimensions for solids and liquids.

THERMAL EXPANSION AND CONTRACTION

As mentioned in Chapter 12, all substances consist of tiny particles or molecules. These molecules are in continuous motion and therefore each contains a store of kinetic energy.

When a substance is heated (i.e. has its temperature raised) its molecules gain in kinetic energy and because of their more rapid movement they usually require additional space in which to exist. Thus the substance expands in size. Conversely, as the temperature is lowered there is a corresponding contraction in size.

LINEAR EXPANSION

If a bar of material is held at one end and heated uniformly, the increase in its length and change in temperature can be measured by the method shown in Fig. 13.1. From such an experiment it is found that the increase in length is proportional to the original length and the rise in temperature. That is,

$$L - L_0 \text{ is proportional to } L_0\Delta\theta$$

or

$$L - L_0 = \alpha L_0 \Delta\theta \qquad [13.1]$$

where $\Delta\theta$ = rise in temperature

L_0 = original length

L = final length

α = coefficient of linear expansion or expansivity which is roughly constant for any one material.

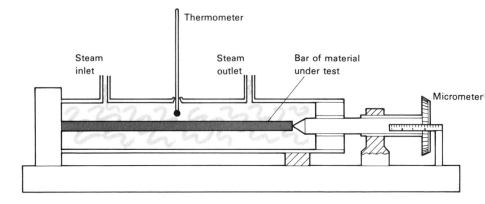

Fig. 13.1   Apparatus to detect the change in length of a metal bar when it is heated

From equation [13.1]

$$L = L_0(1 + \alpha\Delta\theta) \qquad [13.2]$$

If there is a temperature fall, equation [13.2] becomes

$$L = L_0(1 - \alpha\Delta\theta) \qquad [13.3]$$

Values of α denote the increase in length of a bar of unit length per degree Celsius change in temperature. They have to be determined experimentally and some values of α are given in Table 13.1.

TABLE 13.1

Material	Coefficient of linear expansion/$^\circ$C. α
Aluminium	0.000 023
Brass	0.000 019
Copper	0.000 017
Glass	0.000 008 6
Gold	0.000 014
Invar	0.000 001
Iron	0.000 012
Platinum	0.000 008 6
Silver	0.000 019
Steel	0.000 011
Tungsten	0.000 004 5
Zinc	0.000 030

WORKED EXAMPLE 1

A copper pipe in a central heating system is 9 metres long at 15 °C. Find the increase in its length when it is heated to 81 °C by hot water passing through it. (The coefficient of linear expansion for copper is 0.000 017 per °C.)

SOLUTION

Using equation [13.1] gives

$$\text{Expansion} = \alpha L_0 \Delta\theta$$
$$= 0.000\,017 \times 9 \times (81 - 15)$$
$$= 0.000\,017 \times 9 \times 66$$
$$= 0.010 \text{ metres}$$

WORKED EXAMPLE 2

A steel shaft is 125 mm in diameter at 12 °C. What will be its diameter at 32 °C? (The coefficient of linear expansion for steel is 0.000 011 per °C.)

SOLUTION

Using equation [13.2] gives

$$L = L_0(1 + \alpha\Delta\theta)$$
$$= 125 \times (1 + 0.000\,011 \times 20)$$
$$= 125 \times 1.000\,22$$
$$= 125.0275 \text{ mm}$$

Hence the diameter of the shaft at 32 °C is 125.0275 mm.

WORKED EXAMPLE 3

A brass strip is to be made by rolling a brass slab and cutting off the ends when hot. If the strip is to be 20 metres long at 15 °C, what must be the length to which it is cut at 550 °C? (The coefficient of linear expansion of brass is 0.000 019 per °C.)

SOLUTION

Using equation [13.3] gives

$$L = L_0(1 - \alpha\Delta\theta)$$
$$20 = L_0(1 - 0.000\,019 \times 535)$$
$$20 = 0.9898 L_0$$
$$L_0 = \frac{20}{0.9898} = 20.205 \text{ metres}$$

Hence the length at 550°C must be 20.205 m.

THE VOLUMETRIC EXPANSION OF A SOLID _____

Consider a cube of material of side 1 m. If this is heated through 1 °C, the sides become $(1 + \alpha)$ and the new volume is

$$(1 + \alpha)^3 = (1 + 3\alpha + 3\alpha^2 + \alpha^3) \text{cubic metres}$$

Now α is a very small quantity and hence we may ignore α^2 and α^3 as being too small to have any significance. Hence we may take the new volume as being $(1 + 3\alpha)$. Therefore

Change in unit volume per °C $= 3\alpha$

Thus 3α is the fractional change in volume per 1 °C, and it is known as the coefficient of cubical expansion and is denoted by γ (the Greek letter gamma). Thus $\gamma = 3\alpha$.

If V_0 = the original volume of the solid

and V = the final volume of the solid

then $V = V_0(1 + \gamma\Delta\theta)$ [13.4]

WORKED EXAMPLE 4

A glass vessel whose walls are thin has a cubic capacity of 1000 cm³ when the temperature is 15 °C. What will be its capacity when the temperature is raised to 100 °C? Assume that α for glass is 0.000 008 6 per °C.

SOLUTION

Using equation [13.4] gives

$V = V_0(1 + \gamma\Delta\theta)$ where $\gamma = 3\alpha = 3 \times 0.000\,008\,6 = 0.000\,025\,8/°C$

$= 1000 \times (1 + 0.000\,025\,8 \times 85)$

$= 1000 \times 1.002\,193$

$= 1002.193$

Hence the capacity of the vessel at 100 °C is 1002.193 cm³.

THE REAL AND APPARENT EXPANSIONS OF A LIQUID _____

In Worked Example 4 the increase in the cubic capacity of the glass vessel is given by $1002.193 - 1000 = 2.193$ cm³. This is the actual or real expansion which the vessel has undergone.

THE COEFFICIENT OF REAL EXPANSION OF A LIQUID _____

Similarly, liquids when heated undergo volumetric expansion. If the actual expansion of a liquid was known it could be used to find the coefficient of real (or actual) expansion of the liquid since this coefficient is a measure of the fraction of its volume by which the liquid really expands per degree rise in temperature.

However, all liquids must be contained within some form of vessel and the vessel itself will expand when heated. This means that if a liquid actually expands more than its containing vessel its surface level will rise within the vessel and some liquid may even spill over. If the liquid actually expands less than the vessel, its level will fall within the vessel. Thus the expansion of the vessel reduces the actual expansion of the liquid and the observer only sees an apparent expansion (or contraction) of the liquid.

THE APPARENT COEFFICIENT OF VOLUMETRIC EXPANSION

An apparent coefficient of volumetric expansion is therefore spoken of in the case of liquids, and this can be defined as a measure of the fraction of its volume by which the liquid appears to expand for each degree rise in temperature.

It follows from what has been written that

$$\begin{pmatrix} \text{Real expansion} \\ \text{of a liquid} \end{pmatrix} = \begin{pmatrix} \text{Apparent expansion} \\ \text{of the liquid} \end{pmatrix} + \begin{pmatrix} \text{Volumetric expansion} \\ \text{of the vessel} \end{pmatrix}$$

and so

$$\begin{pmatrix} \text{Real coefficient} \\ \text{of volumetric} \\ \text{expansion of a} \\ \text{liquid} \end{pmatrix} = \begin{pmatrix} \text{Apparent coefficient} \\ \text{of expansion of the} \\ \text{liquid} \end{pmatrix} + \begin{pmatrix} \text{Coefficient of} \\ \text{volumetric expansion} \\ \text{of the vessel} \end{pmatrix}$$

WORKED EXAMPLE 5

A flask at a temperature of 15 °C is filled with a liquid at the same temperature. The flask is then closed with a bung, through which passes a length of open glass tubing so that any liquid displaced by the bung is forced a short distance up the tube. The flask, which has a capacity of 1000 at 15 °C, is now warmed, together with the liquid it contains, until the temperature is 80 °C. It is then observed that the level of liquid in the tube has risen by

25 cm. If each centimetre rise in level represents an apparent expansion of 0.5 cm^3 of the liquid, calculate the amount by which the liquid has really expanded and its coefficients of real and apparent volumetric expansion. Neglect any effect due to the expansion of the tube. The coefficient of linear expansion of glass is $0.000\,008\,6/°C$.

SOLUTION

Let V_0 be the original volume of the glass vessel.

Let V be the final volume of the glass vessel

Then, from Equation [13.4],

$$V - V_0 = V_0 \gamma \Delta\theta$$
$$= 1000 \times 3 \times 0.000\,008\,6 \times 65$$
$$= 1.677 \text{ cm}^3$$

$$\text{Apparent expansion of liquid} = 25 \times 0.5$$
$$= 12.5 \text{ cm}^3$$

Therefore

$$\text{Real expansion of liquid} = 12.5 + 1.677$$
$$= 14.177 \text{ cm}^3$$

Hence

$$\left(\begin{array}{c} \text{Coefficient of apparent} \\ \text{volumetric expansion} \\ \text{of the liquid} \end{array} \right) = \frac{12.5}{1000 \times 65}$$
$$= 0.000\,192/°C$$

and

$$\left(\begin{array}{c} \text{Coefficient of real} \\ \text{volumetric expansion} \\ \text{of the liquid} \end{array} \right) = \frac{14.177}{1000 \times 65}$$
$$= 0.000\,218/°C$$

EXERCISE 13

1)   Determine the coefficient of linear expansion of the metal of a bar whose length at $20°C$ was $100\,\text{mm}$ and whose length at $100°C$ is $100.128\,\text{mm}$.

2)   A copper bar has a diameter of $120\,\text{mm}$ at $15°C$. Find its diameter at $285°C$ if the coefficient of linear expansion of copper is $0.000\,017$ per $°C$.

3)   A steam pipe is 12 m long at 15°C. Determine its length when carrying steam at 420°C. The coefficient of linear expansion of steel is 0.000 011 per °C.

4)   A bronze collar is to be shrunk on to a steel shaft 150 mm diameter. The collar is bored to 149.88 mm diameter and is to be heated until the bore is 150.38 mm in order to slide freely on the shaft. Calculate the temperature to which the collar must be raised from a temperature of 15°C. The coefficient of linear expansion of bronze is 0.000 018 per °C.

5)   A steel strip is to be made by rolling a billet and cutting off the ends whilst hot. If the strip is to be 25 m long at 15°C, what must be the length to which it is cut at 800°C? The coefficient of linear expansion for steel is 0.000 011 per °C.

6)   A steel tyre is 1.75 m in diameter when the temperature is 200°C. Calculate the temperature to which it must be raised to make its diameter 1.76 m. The coefficient of linear expansion of steel is 0.000 011 per °C.

7)   A heat exchanger has brass tubes which are 2 m long when fitted at a room temperature of 15°C. What length will the tubes be when cooling water at 4°C is passed through them? The coefficient of linear expansion of brass is 0.000 019 per °C.

8)   Two pieces of metal, one steel and the other aluminium are 1000 mm and 999 mm long respectively at 20°C. (a) At what temperature will they be the same length? (b) What will be their lengths at this temperature? The coefficients of linear expansion for steel and aluminium are 0.000 011 and 0.000 023 per °C respectively.

9)   A cube of cast iron of side 50 mm has an initial temperature of 20°C. If its temperature is raised to 250°C, calculate the change in volume of the cube given that the coefficient of linear expansion for cast iron is 0.000 012.

10)   A glass flask and tube of total capacity 1 litre are filled with oil at 20°C. The temperature is then lowered to 15°C. If the area of cross-section of the tube is 1 cm², find the change in level of the oil in the tube. (Coefficient of linear expansion of glass = 0.000 008 per °C; coefficient of real expansion of oil = 0.000 544 per °C.)

11)   A flask at a temperature of 20°C is filled with a liquid at the same temperature. The flask is then closed with a bung through which passes a length of open glass tubing so that a small quantity of the liquid is forced a short distance up the tube. The flask, which when fitted with the bung has a capacity of 1000 cm^3 at 20°C, is now heated until the temperature of the flask and liquid is 90°C. If each centimetre rise in the level of liquid in the tube represents an apparent expansion of 0.4 cm^3 of liquid, calculate the rise in the level of liquid in the tube. Neglect any effect due to the expansion of the tube itself and the liquid actually in the tube. (Coefficient of real expansion of glass = 0.000 008 6 per °C. Coefficient of real expansion of the liquid = 0.0003 per °C.)

12)   A glass vessel has an internal volume of 32 cm^3 of which 4 cm^3 is occupied by mercury. If the temperature changes from 15°C to 75°C, determine: (a) the change in volume of the flask, (b) the change in volume of the mercury. (Coefficient of linear expansion of glass = 0.000 009 per °C. Coefficient of real expansion of mercury = 0.000 189 per °C.)

13)   A rectangular block of aluminium measures 25 × 15 × 10 mm at 15°C. Find the volume of the block if its temperature is raised to 185°C. The coefficient of linear expansion of aluminium is 0.000 023 per °C.

14)   A flask at a temperature of 20°C is filled with liquid at the same temperature. The flask is then closed with a stopper through which passes a length of open glass tubing so that any liquid displaced by the stopper is forced a short distance up the tube. The flask, which has a capacity of 1000 cm^3 at 20°C is now heated until its temperature is 85°C. It is then noted that the level of liquid in the tube has risen by 22 cm. If each centimetre rise in level in the tube represents an apparent expansion of 0.5 cm^3 of the liquid, calculate the amount by which the liquid has really expanded and find its coefficients of real and apparent volumetric expansion. Neglect any effect due to the expansion of the tube. The coefficient of linear expansion of glass is 0.000 009 per °C.

14 MACHINES

After reaching the end of this chapter you should be able to:

1. Describe a machine as a device for changing the magnitude and line of action of a force.
2. Describe, with the aid of sketches, the construction of (a) a pulley system, (b) a screw jack, (c) a gear system.
3. Solve simple lever problems.
4. Define (a) force ratio (mechanical advantage), (b) movement ratio (velocity ratio), (c) efficiency and solve problems involving these quantities in relation to simple machines.
5. Investigate experimentally a machine and use the results to plot graphs of effort, force ratio and efficiency against load (the load being the independent variable).
6. Deduce the limiting efficiency of the machine used in 5.
7. Explain why the efficiency cannot reach 100%.

WHAT A MACHINE IS

A machine is an assemblage of simple parts such as rods, pulleys, gear wheels, cables and screws. These are connected to each other in such a manner that when a force (the effort) is applied at one point to the system a second force is produced at some other point and made to overcome a resistance or load. When movement takes place work is said to be done *on* the machine at the point where the effort is applied and *by* the machine at the point where the machine overcomes the resistance. A machine therefore, is also a device which enables work or energy to be transferred from one point to another.

MECHANICAL ADVANTAGE

A machine can be designed so that a small effort will enable a large resistance or load to be overcome. This undoubted advantage is referred to as the *mechanical advantage* or the *force ratio* of the machine and is measured as follows:

$$\text{Mechanical advantage (MA)} = \frac{\text{Resistance overcome}}{\text{Applied force}}$$

or, more briefly

$$\text{MA} = \frac{\text{Load}}{\text{Effort}} \qquad [14.1]$$

In all actual machines the value of MA will vary with the friction, the load and the 'useless' load (weight of moving parts of the machine, for example the pulleys). This is because the effort has to overcome both the useful load, friction and 'useless' load.

VELOCITY RATIO

Since machines are composed of rigid links, any movement of the effort and the corresponding movement made by the machine in overcoming the resistance occur in the same time.

Let t = the time for these movements. Then

$$\text{Velocity of effort} = \frac{\text{Distance moved by effort}}{t}$$

and

$$\text{Velocity of load} = \frac{\text{Distance moved by load}}{t}$$

The ratio of these velocities is defined as follows:

$$\text{Velocity ratio (VR)} = \frac{\text{Distance moved by effort}}{\text{Distance moved by load}} \qquad [14.2]$$

since the times, being the same for both movements, cancel.

Velocity ratio as expressed by equation [14.2] is strictly a *movement* ratio but in certain instances true velocity ratios are required as, for instance, when speed reduction values for gears are considered.

The velocity ratio is constant for any one machine arrangement since it is dependent only on the geometry of the machine parts.

MACHINE EFFICIENCY

Unfortunately with all machines there are losses of mechanical energy during transmission. These are partly due to friction which is always present between the moving parts and also to 'useless' load. The smaller the losses in a given type of machine the more efficient that machine is said to be. Efficiency, therefore, is a means of measuring how successful a machine is in transferring energy from the point where it is put into the system to the point where it is taken out, that is,

$$\text{Efficiency } \eta = \frac{\text{Energy got out of machine}}{\text{Energy put into machine}} \qquad [14.3]$$

or, since energy is simply the ability to do work:

$$\text{Efficiency} = \frac{\text{Work got out of machine}}{\text{Work put into machine}} \qquad [14.4]$$

or

$$\text{Efficiency} = \frac{\text{Load} \times \text{Distance moved by load}}{\text{Effort} \times \text{Distance moved by effort}} \qquad [14.5]$$

Rearranging Equation [14.5] gives

$$\text{Efficiency} = \frac{\text{Load}}{\text{Effort}} \times \frac{\text{Distance moved by load}}{\text{Distance moved by effort}}$$

$$= \frac{\text{Mechanical advantage}}{1} \times \frac{1}{\text{Velocity ratio}}$$

More briefly

$$\text{Efficiency } \eta = \frac{\text{MA}}{\text{VR}} \qquad [14.6]$$

Efficiency is expressed as a fraction or as a percentage and for an actual machine is always less than unity or 100%.

Under *ideal*, i.e. frictionless, conditions or when friction and 'useless' load can be neglected, the efficiency = 1, and then, numerically, the mechanical advantage equals the velocity ratio.

IDEAL EFFORT

In an ideal machine, therefore,

$$\frac{\text{Work got out of machine}}{\text{Work put into machine}} = 1$$

or

$$\text{Work got out} = \text{Work put in}$$

Under these ideal conditions the effort exerted is referred to as the *ideal effort*, so that

$$\text{Ideal effort} \times \text{Distance moved by effort} = \text{Load} \times \text{Distance moved by load}$$

or

$$\text{Ideal effort} = \text{Load} \times \frac{\text{Distance moved by load}}{\text{Distance moved by effort}} \qquad [14.7]$$

or

$$\text{Ideal effort} = \text{Load} \times \frac{1}{\text{Velocity ratio}} \qquad [14.8]$$

Hence, in the case of an actual machine where friction is present:

$$\begin{pmatrix} \text{Effort required to overcome} \\ \text{friction plus 'useless' load} \end{pmatrix} = \text{Actual effort} - \text{Ideal effort} \qquad [14.9]$$

BASIC TYPES OF MACHINES

LEVERS

Probably the most elementary types of machines are levers. These are of three kinds or *orders* distinguished by the position of the fulcrum in relation to where the effort and the force exerted in overcoming the resistance are applied.

Thus, referring to Fig. 14.1 show that:

A *first-order lever* (a) has the fulcrum F between the effort and load points A and B respectively.

A *second-order lever* (b) has the load point B between the effort point A and fulcrum F.

A *third-order lever* (c) has the effort point A between load point B and fulcrum F.

In each case, neglecting friction and the weight of the lever, the ideal effort can be found by taking moments about the fulcrum F, so that

$$\text{Ideal effort} \times AF = \text{Load} \times BF$$

$$\text{Ideal effort} = \text{Load} \times \frac{BF}{AF}$$

Alternatively, using Equation [14.7] and remembering that arc $= r\theta$, then since the distances moved by the effort and the load are proportional to the arcs $a_1 a_2$ and $b_1 b_2$ respectively:

$$\text{Ideal effort} = \frac{\text{Load} \times \text{Arc } b_1 b_2}{\text{Arc } a_1 a_2}$$

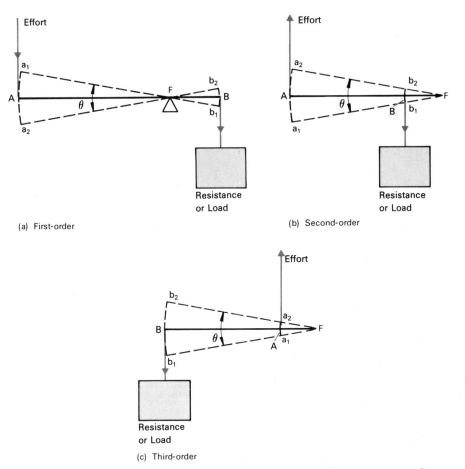

(a) First-order

(b) Second-order

(c) Third-order

Fig. 14.1   The three systems of levers

$$= \text{Load} \times \frac{\text{BF} \times \theta}{\text{AF} \times \theta}$$

$$= \text{Load} \times \frac{\text{BF}}{\text{AF}} \quad \text{as before}$$

Examples of first-order levers are: the crow bar, the claw hammer when used for removing nails, a pair of scissors, a bell crank lever and, as a more advanced application, a scissor lift (see Fig. 14.2). Second-order levers include: nut crackers, the brake handle of a bicycle and as more advanced applications the internal expanding shoe brake of a motor car, a stone crusher (Fig. 14.3) and a foot-pump (Fig. 14.4). Examples of third-order levers are: a pair of forceps, some forms of screw clamps and the stroke link of a shaping machine (Fig. 14.5).

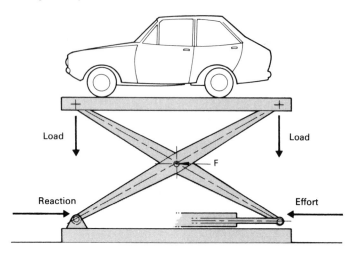

Fig. 14.2   The scissor lift

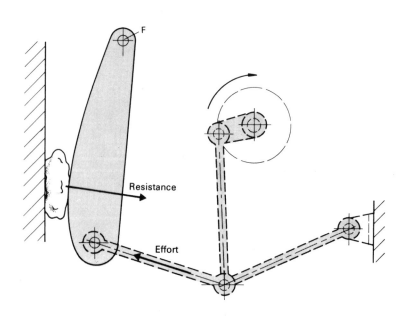

Fig. 14.3   A stone crusher

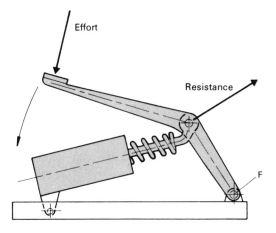

Fig. 14.4   A foot pump

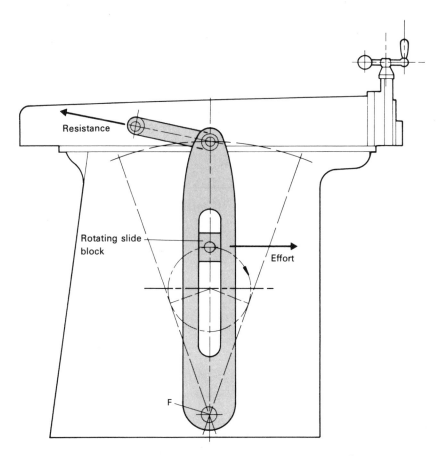

Fig. 14.5   The stroke link of a shaping machine

WORKED EXAMPLE 1

In the three orders of levers shown in Fig. 14.1 (a), (b) and (c) the following dimensions are known:

$$\text{For a first-order lever } AF = 800 \text{ mm}; \quad BF = 200 \text{ mm}$$
$$\text{For a second-order lever } AF = 800 \text{ mm}; \quad BF = 200 \text{ mm}$$
$$\text{For a third-order lever } AF = 200 \text{ mm}; \quad BF = 800 \text{ mm}$$

If in each case an effort of 40 N is exerted at A, find for each type of lever: (a) the resistance overcome, (b) the mechanical advantage, and (c) the velocity ratio. Assume that the levers have negligible weight.

SOLUTION

For first- and second-order levers:

(a) $\text{Load} = \text{Effort} \times \dfrac{AF}{BF} = 40 \times \dfrac{800}{200} = 160 \text{ N}$

(b) $\text{Mechanical advantage} = \dfrac{\text{Load}}{\text{Effort}} = \dfrac{160}{40} = 4$

(c) $\text{Velocity ratio} = \dfrac{\text{Arc } a_1 a_2}{\text{Arc } b_1 b_2}$

$\qquad = \dfrac{AF\theta}{BF\theta} = \dfrac{800}{200} = 4$

The answers are the same for the two orders of lever but note the change in the direction of the effort needed in order to lift the load.

For the third-order lever:

(a) $\text{Load} = \text{Effort} \times \dfrac{AF}{BF} = 40 \times \dfrac{200}{800} = 10 \text{ N}$

(b) $\text{Mechanical advantage} = \dfrac{\text{Load}}{\text{Effort}} = \dfrac{10}{40} = 0.25$

(c) $\text{Velocity ratio} = \dfrac{AF\theta}{BF\theta} = \dfrac{200}{800} = 0.25$

PULLEY SYSTEMS

A pulley is a grooved wheel pivoted about its centre.

Pulleys can be arranged to give various basic systems. This is done by using cord, cable or chain to link them together. Different systems provide different mechanical advantages and velocity ratios. In each of the following cases the velocity ratio is dependent only on the geometrical configuration but, as already mentioned, the mechanical advantage will vary with friction, with 'useless' load and the load being lifted. In each case too, it is assumed that the pulleys are frictionless and without weight (i.e. there is no 'useless' load) and that the cords joining them are inextensible.

THE PRINCIPLE OF WORK _____

Under frictionless conditions there is no loss of energy within a machine. Therefore, the principle of work can be applied. This states that

> Work done on the machine = Work done by the machine

Case I

The single fixed pulley arrangement shown in Fig. 14.6 simply changes the direction of the force F. The load will equal the effort and the distances moved by the load and effort are the same. Therefore $MA = VR = 1$.

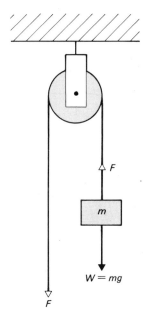

Fig. 14.6   A single fixed pulley arrangement

Case II

In Fig. 14.7 the single pulley is now movable. By applying an effort to the free end of the cord let the mass m be raised by b mm. Then *both* sides of the supporting cord must shorten by b mm. Since one end of this cord is fastened the free end, and hence the effort must move upwards a distance of $2b$ mm.

$$\text{VR} = \frac{\text{Distance moved by effort}}{\text{Distance moved by load}}$$

$$= \frac{2b}{b} = 2$$

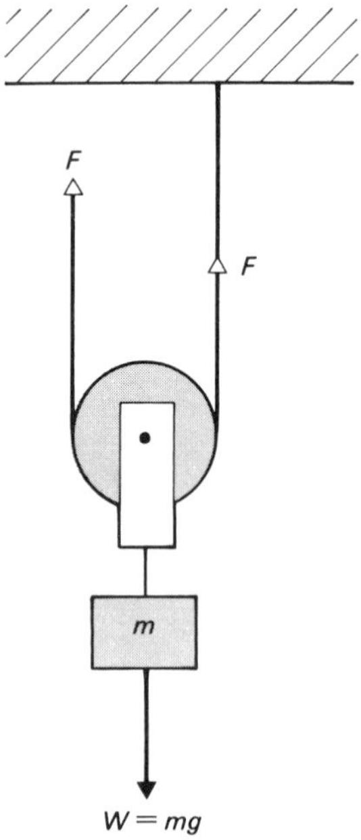

Fig. 14.7   A single movable pulley arrangement

Since the load is supported by two cords each with tension F,

$$W = 2F$$

Therefore

$$\text{MA} = \frac{W}{F} = 2$$

The same result could be obtained by applying the principle of work:

$$\text{Work done by machine} = \text{Work done on machine}$$

Therefore

$$Wb = F \times 2b$$

Therefore
$$MA = \frac{W}{F} = \frac{2b}{b} = 2$$

Case III

Refer to Fig. 14.8. By applying a force F (the effort) to the free end of the cord let m be raised b mm. Then pulley P_1 must rise b mm. Hence pulley P_2 must rise $2b$ mm to take up the slack in *both* sides of the cord supporting pulley P_1. Similarly pulley P_3 must rise $4b$ mm to take up the slack in *both* sides of the cord supporting pulley P_2. Hence $8b$ mm of cord must pass over P_4 to take up the slack in both sides of the cord supporting pulley P_3. Then

$$VR = \frac{\text{Distance moved by effort}}{\text{Distance moved by load}}$$

$$= \frac{8b}{b} = 8$$

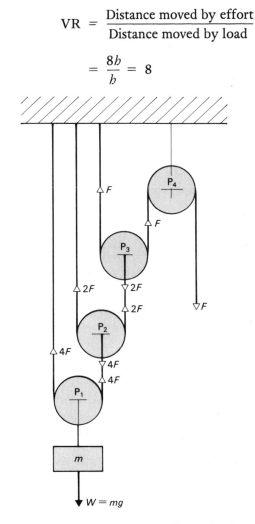

Fig. 14.8   A set of movable pulleys

Also, by applying the principle of work,

Work done on the machine = Work done by the machine

$$F \times 8h = W \times h$$

$$\text{MA} = \frac{W}{F} = 8$$

Note that the relationship $W = 8F$ may also be deduced by considering the tensions in the cords (see Fig. 14.8).

Case IV

Referring to Fig. 14.9 (opposite). At section AA there are six parts of the cord supporting the mass m of weight W. The tension in the cord will be the same throughout because of the frictionless conditions assumed. Therefore

$$\text{Effort } F = \frac{\text{Total load}}{\text{Number of supporting cords}} = \frac{W}{6}$$

$$\text{MA} = \frac{W}{F} = 6$$

and for frictionless conditions

$$\text{VR} = \text{MA} = 6$$

By making the upper three pulleys equal in diameter and arranging them side by side within one block on a common axle and doing the same with the bottom three pulleys a practical block and tackle is obtained (Fig. 14.10, p. 266). The velocity ratio remains unchanged.

THE WESTON DIFFERENTIAL PULLEY

In this arrangement (Fig. 14.11, p. 267) two pulleys of different diameters are fastened together and rotate as one on a common axle. An endless chain passes over these pulleys and also around a movable pulley which supports the mass m being lifted. The chain engages with teeth in the upper pulleys which prevent slip.

Let D and d be the diameters of the differential pulley. Then, when a pull F is applied as shown the differential pulley will rotate clockwise causing the chain to be wound on to the larger pulley and off the smaller one resulting in a net shortening of chain supporting the lower pulley. For one complete revolution of the differential pulley the amount by which the supporting

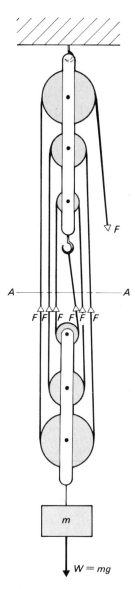

Fig. 14.9   A block and tackle arrangement

chain is shortened equals $\pi(D-d)$. Hence the load rises through $(\pi/2)(D-d)$, and the distance moved by the effort equals the length of chain wound off the larger pulley — that is, πD.

Therefore

$$\text{VR} = \frac{\pi D}{(\pi/2)(D-d)} = \frac{2D}{(D-d)} \qquad [14.10]$$

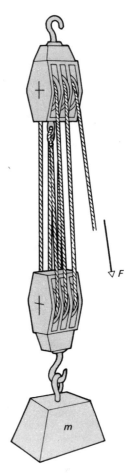

Fig. 14.10   A practical block and tackle

As the difference between D and d is made smaller, the denominator in Equation [14.10] becomes smaller and hence the velocity ratio becomes larger. Since MA = VR for frictionless conditions, the the MA increases when $(D-d)$ is made smaller. Thus to lift large loads using small efforts, the two pulleys must have similar diameters.

WORKED EXAMPLE 2

A block and tackle has a differential pulley whose effective diameters are 300 and 280 mm. Friction is present and it is found that in order to raise a mass whose weight is 1000 N a force of 50 N must be exerted on the 'fall' of the chain. Find: (a) the velocity ratio, (b) the mechanical advantage, (c) the efficiency, (d) the ideal effort, and (e) the effort required to overcome friction. Assume the weight of the moving pulley can be neglected.

SOLUTION

(a) $\displaystyle VR = \frac{2D}{D-d} = \frac{2 \times 300}{300-280} = \frac{600}{20} = 30$

(b) $\displaystyle MA = \frac{\text{Load}}{\text{Effort}} = \frac{1000}{50} = 20$

(c) $\displaystyle \text{Efficiency} = \frac{MA}{VR} = \frac{20}{30} = 0.666 = 66.6\%$

(d) $\displaystyle \text{Ideal effort} = \frac{\text{Load}}{VR} = \frac{1000}{30} = 33.3 \, N$

(e) Effort required to overcome friction = Actual effort − Ideal effort

$$= 50 - 33.3$$
$$= 16.7 \, N$$

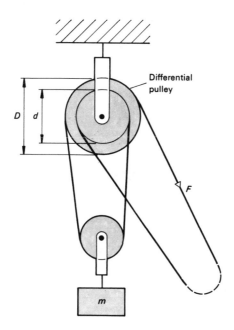

Fig. 14.11   The Weston differential pulley

THE WHEEL AND AXLE

This simple type of lifting machine is shown in Fig. 14.12. Let D be the diameter of the effort wheel and d the diameter of the axle supporting the load. For equilibrium under frictionless conditions taking moments about the axis of rotation:

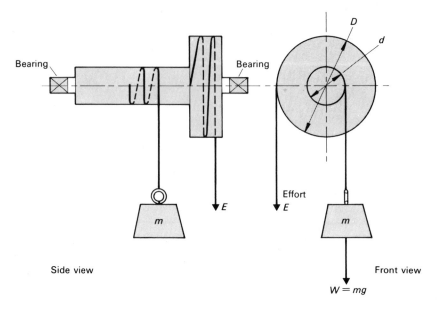

Fig. 14.12   The wheel and axle

$$E \times \frac{D}{2} = W \times \frac{d}{2}$$

i.e.
$$MA = \frac{W}{E} = \frac{D}{d}$$ [14.11]

Also, for one revolution of the wheel and axle

Distance moved by effort   =   Length of cord unwound from the wheel

= πD

Distance moved by load   =   Length of cord wound on to the axle

= πd

$$VR = \frac{\pi D}{\pi d} = \frac{D}{d}$$ [14.12]

WORKED EXAMPLE 3

A wheel and axle has a wheel diameter of 300 mm and an axle diameter of 100 mm. When lifting a mass of 40 kg it is found that an effort of 150 N is needed. Calculate: (a) the velocity ratio, (b) the mechanical advantage and (c) the efficiency of the system.

SOLUTION

(a) $VR = \dfrac{D}{d} = \dfrac{300}{100} = 3$

(b)   Load $W = mg = 40 \times 9.81 = 392.4\ N$

$MA = \dfrac{W}{E} = \dfrac{392.4}{150} = 2.616$

(c)   Efficiency $= \dfrac{MA}{VR} = \dfrac{2.616}{3} = 0.872$ or

$= 87.2\%$

THE DIFFERENTIAL WHEEL AND AXLE

This type of wheel and axle (Fig. 14.13) gives a much higher velocity ratio and mechanical advantage than the simpler kind shown in Fig. 14.12.

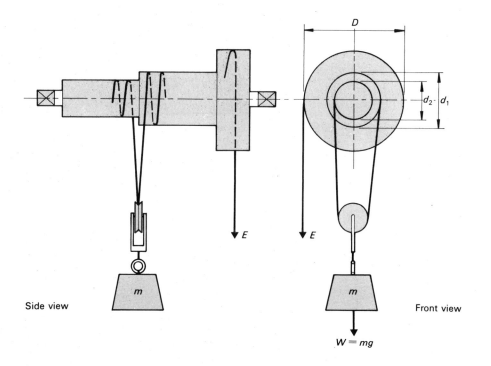

Side view

Front view

$W = mg$

Fig. 14.13   The differential wheel and axle

Let d_1 and d_2 be the larger and smaller diameters of the axle and D the diameter of the wheel. For one complete rotation in the direction shown:

Length of cord unwound from smaller axle $= \pi d_2$

Length of cord wound on to larger axle $= \pi d_1$

Total shortening of the rope $= \pi d_1 - \pi d_2 = \pi(d_1 - d_2)$

This loss of rope is shared equally by the two supporting lengths of rope.

Therefore

Height through which the load rises $= \dfrac{\pi}{2}(d_1 - d_2)$

Meanwhile

Distance moved by the effort $= \pi D$

Therefore

$$\text{VR} = \frac{\pi D}{\pi/2\,(d_1 - d_2)} = \frac{2D}{(d_1 - d_2)} \qquad [14.13]$$

When friction is present the MA will vary with the load lifted but under ideal conditions is equal numerically to the VR.

THE SCREW JACK

In this kind of lifting device (Fig. 14.14) the load is raised by rotating the screw in the fixed body which forms the nut.

The pitch of the thread is the distance between corresponding points on adjacent thread turns measured parallel to the axis of the thread. The lead of a thread is the axial distance that the thread moves in one revolution. A single start thread has the lead equal to the pitch (Fig. 14.15) but for a multi-start thread (Fig. 14.16)

Lead $=$ Pitch $\times$ Number of starts

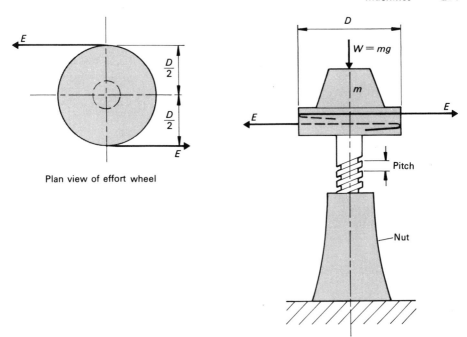

Plan view of effort wheel

Fig. 14.14   The screw jack

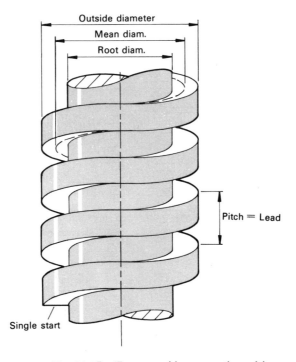

Fig. 14.15   Terms used in connection with a screw thread

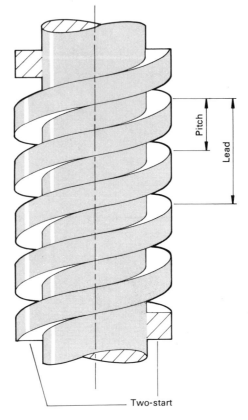

Fig. 14.16   A two-start thread

The effort can be applied as shown by means of two cords wound in opposite directions around the effort wheel. In this way any sideways pull on the thread is avoided.

To find the velocity ratio of the screw jack, give the effort wheel one complete revolution. Then

Distance moved by the effort = Circumference of circle traced by effort

$$= \pi D$$

Distance moved by the load = Lead of thread

$$\text{VR} = \frac{\text{Distance moved by effort}}{\text{Distance moved by load}} = \frac{D}{\text{Lead}} \qquad [14.14]$$

Also, for frictionless conditions, MA = VR.

SPUR GEAR SYSTEMS

Sometimes it is necessary to transmit rotary motion from one shaft to another. When the shafts are parallel and close enough to each other the best way is often by means of spur gears. These are gear wheels whose teeth are parallel to the axis of rotation. The teeth on each wheel are shaped so that they roll and slide smoothly over each other when engaged. They are spaced or 'pitched' equally around the circumferences of their wheels to enable a tooth on one wheel to fit accurately into a space between two teeth on the other (Fig. 14.17). Slipping cannot occur and the accuracy of fit provides a continuous constant velocity ratio between any two engaging wheels. The circles on which the teeth are spaced or pitched are known as the 'pitch' or 'reference' circles. These important circles represent the effective sizes of the wheels.

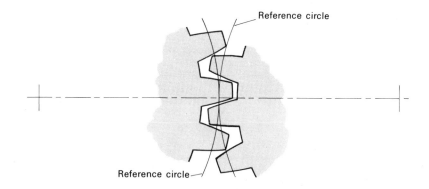

Fig. 14.17   The meshing of teeth on spur gears

Figs. 14.18 and 14.19 show two systems of gears. In Fig. 14.18 the shafts are directly connected by the wheels A and B which are keyed to them. The shafts therefore rotate in opposite directions. In Fig. 14.19 an intermediate wheel (or idler wheel), I, mounted on a third shaft transmits rotation from A to B. Because of this intermediate wheel the driving and driven shafts now rotate in the same direction.

Refer first to Fig. 14.18. Let the smaller wheel A (the pinion) have 20 teeth and the larger wheel B 40 teeth. Let the effort be applied to A thus making it the effort or driving wheel. Wheel B, the driven wheel, can then be thought of as the load wheel. During one complete rotation of A all its 20 teeth will engage with 20 of B's 40 teeth so that B will only make 20/40 or one half a revolution.

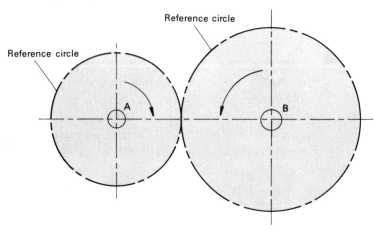

Fig. 14.18   The reference circles for spur gears

Therefore

$$VR = \frac{\text{Angular distance moved by effort wheel}}{\text{Angular distance moved by load wheel}}$$

$$VR = \frac{\text{Revolutions of driver}}{\text{Revolutions of driven}} \qquad [14.15]$$

In this case

$$VR = \frac{N_A}{N_B} = \frac{1}{\frac{1}{2}} = 2$$

where N_A and N_B refer to the number of revolutions made by wheels A and B respectively in the same time.

Refer next to Fig. 14.19. Let I have n teeth.

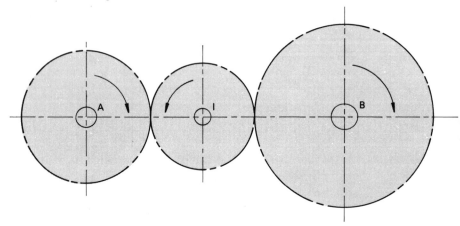

Fig. 14.19   An idler wheel I, incorporated so that A and B rotate in the same direction

Then, in a manner similar to the previous reasoning,

$$\text{if A makes one revolution, I will make } \frac{20}{n} \text{ revs}$$

but

$$\text{if I makes one revolution, B will make } \frac{n}{40} \text{ revs}$$

Therefore

$$\text{since I makes } \frac{20}{n} \text{ revolutions, B will make } \frac{20}{n} \times \frac{n}{40} = \frac{1}{2} \text{ rev}$$

$$\text{VR of whole system} = \frac{\text{Revolutions of A}}{\text{Revolutions of B}}$$

$$= \frac{1}{\frac{1}{2}} = 2 \quad \text{as before}$$

That is, the intermediate wheel I has no effect on the numerical value of the velocity ratio. Because of this it is usually referred to as an *idler* or *idle wheel*. It does however change the direction of rotation of B relative to A.

Note also

$$\text{VR} = \frac{\text{Number of teeth in driven wheel}}{\text{Number of teeth in driving wheel}} \qquad [14.16]$$

and, since the number of teeth in a wheel is proportional to the length of the circumference of the wheel which in turn is proportional to its diameter, then

$$\text{VR} = \frac{\text{Diameter of driven wheel}}{\text{Diameter of driving wheel}} \qquad [14.17]$$

WORM AND WHEEL

Fig. 14.20 shows a worm and wheel. The worm is a screw gear which engages with teeth in the circumference of the gear wheel. The effort wheel is integral with the worm and the lifting drum is integral with the gear wheel. One complete rotation of the effort wheel and hence of the worm will cause each tooth on the wheel to be moved around through a distance equal to the lead of the worm thread.

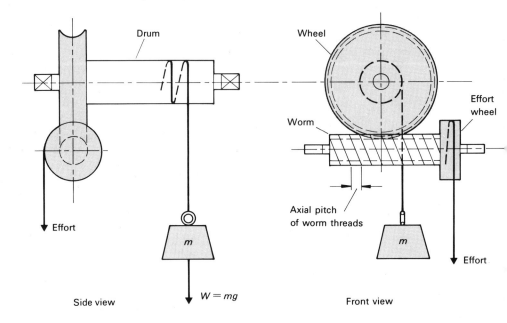

Fig. 14.20   A worm and wheel arrangement

For a single-start worm the lead equals the pitch (refer to p. 270 for an explanation of these terms). Hence if the number of teeth on the wheel is 40, for example, the wheel will rotate through 1/40 of a revolution for one complete rotation of the worm.

Let D = Diameter of the effort wheel

                               d = Diameter of the drum

                               n = Number of teeth in the wheel

Then, assuming that the worm is single-start and that the effort wheel makes one complete revolution:

$$\text{Distance moved by effort} = \pi D$$

$$\text{Rotation of the gear wheel and drum} = \frac{1}{n}\text{ revs}$$

Therefore

$$\text{Angle turned through by gear wheel and drum} = \frac{2\pi}{n}\text{ radians}$$

$$\text{Distance moved by load} = \theta \frac{d}{2}$$

$$= \frac{2\pi}{n} \times \frac{d}{2} = \frac{\pi d}{n}$$

Then

$$\text{VR} = \frac{\text{Distance moved by effort}}{\text{Distance moved by load}}$$

$$= \pi D \div \frac{\pi d}{n}$$

$$= \frac{\pi D n}{\pi d} = \frac{D}{d} \times n$$

Generally, if t = the number of 'starts' on the worm gear,

$$\text{VR} = \frac{D}{d} \times \frac{n}{t} \qquad\qquad [14.18]$$

THE LAW OF A MACHINE

In a machine the effort and the load are related by a straight line equation. This relationship is known as the law of the machine and can be found as shown in the example below:

A test carried out on a machine provided the following values of load and effort. The velocity ratio of the machine was 30.

Load (N)	60	100	150	250	300	350	400	500
Effort (N)	10	12.4	15.4	21.2	24.2	27.2	30.0	36

From the above readings corresponding values of mechanical advantage, efficiency, ideal effort and effort required to overcome friction, etc. were obtained using equations [14.1], [14.6], [14.8] and [14.9] respectively. A complete set of values is tabulated overleaf.

Load (N)	60	100	150	250	300	350	400	500
Effort (N)	10	12.4	15.4	21.2	24.2	27.2	30.0	36.0
MA	6	8.06	9.94	11.79	12.39	12.87	13.33	13.88
VR	30	30	30	30	30	30	30	30
Efficiency (%)	20	27	32	39	41	43	44	46
Ideal effort (N)	2.0	3.33	5.0	8.33	10.0	11.67	13.33	16.66
Friction effort (N)	8.0	9.07	10.4	12.87	14.2	15.53	16.67	19.34

The graph (Fig. 14.21) shows the actual, ideal and friction efforts, mechanical advantage and efficiency plotted against load.

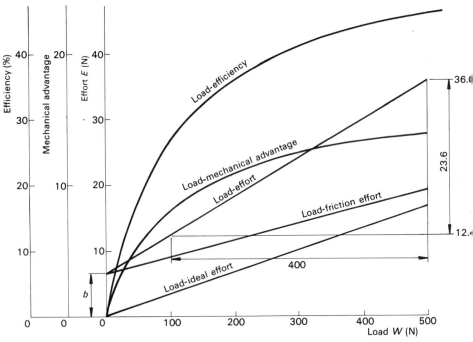

Fig. 14.21   The characteristics of a machine

The load–effort graph is a straight line which intercepts the effort axis at some point above zero effort and has a positive slope. Hence the relationship between the actual effort and the load can be expressed by the straight line equation

$$E = aW + b \qquad [14.19]$$

where

$$E = \text{Actual effort (N)}$$

$$W = \text{Load (N)}$$

$$a = \text{Slope of the graph (a constant)}$$

$$b = \text{Intercept on the effort axis (a constant)}$$

Equation [14.19] is the general form in which the law of a machine is expressed.

For this particular machine the slope a can be obtained by dividing the vertical by the horizontal differences between any two points on the load–effort graph, for example, points $E = 36$, $W = 500$ and $E = 12.4$, $W = 100$, when

$$\text{Slope } A = \frac{36 - 12.4}{500 - 100}$$

$$= \frac{23.6}{400}$$

$$= 0.059$$

The intercept b is read directly from the graph and equals 6.5.

Hence this particular machine obeys the law $E = 0.059W + 6.5$.

THE LIMITING EFFICIENCY OF A MACHINE _____

The shape of the load–efficiency graph of Fig. 14.21 suggests that if the load were continually increased the efficiency of the machine would eventually reach some upper limit.

$$\eta = \text{Efficiency} = \frac{\text{MA}}{\text{VR}} = \frac{W}{E \times \text{VR}}$$

But $E = aW + b$ (Equation [14.19]). Therefore

$$\eta = \frac{W}{(aW + b) \times \text{VR}}$$

Dividing numerator and denominator by W gives

$$\eta = \frac{1}{[a + (b/W)]\,\text{VR}}$$

As W is made bigger, the fraction b/W becomes smaller until, when $W = \infty$, $b/W = 0$, and

$$\eta = \frac{1}{a \, \text{VR}}$$

That is, a lifting machine has a limiting efficiency which is given by the reciprocal of (the constant a multiplied by the VR).

In the above example the limiting efficiency will therefore be

$$\frac{1}{0.059 \times 30} = 0.57 = 57\%$$

OVERHAULING

If the effort is removed during a lifting operation the gravitational pull on the load will tend to cause the lifting machine to run backwards thus causing the load to fall. When a machine does this it is said to *overhaul*. A machine will not overhaul if the frictional forces at the bearings are large enough to prevent this happening.

CONDITIONS FOR OVERHAULING

Consider as a machine the simple pulley shown in Fig. 14.22. Assume that there is friction at bearings B and that a mass m kg, weight mg newtons,

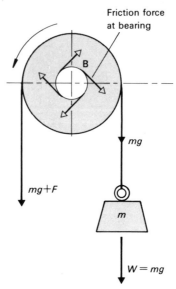

Fig. 14.22   A simple pulley with a weight being pulled

is being raised by a pull on the 'fall' of the rope. Under frictionless conditions a pull equal to mg would be sufficient but because of friction the pull will be $mg + F$, where F is the force at the rope equivalent to the friction force at the bearing. If the load is raised through height h, then

$$\text{Efficiency} = \frac{\text{Work got out of the machine}}{\text{Work put into the machine}}$$

$$\eta = \frac{\text{Load} \times \text{Distance moved by load}}{\text{Effort} \times \text{Distance moved by effort}}$$

$$\eta = \frac{mgh}{(mg + F)h} = \frac{mg}{(mg + F)}$$

$$\eta(mg + F) = mg$$

$$\eta mg + \eta F = mg$$

$$\eta F = mg - \eta mg$$

$$F = \frac{mg}{\eta} - mg$$

or

$$F = mg\left(\frac{1}{\eta} - 1\right) \qquad\qquad [14.20]$$

When the effort is removed the machine tends to run backwards. The friction force which always opposes motion is now reversed. Hence F, the force in the rope equivalent to the friction force, is reversed and opposes the pull mg on the unsupported mass m (Fig. 14.23).

If the machine is not to overhaul:

$$F \text{ must be equal to or greater than } mg.$$

Substituting this condition into equation [14.20] gives

$$mg\left(\frac{1}{\eta} - 1\right) \geqslant mg$$

or

$$\frac{1}{\eta} - 1 \geqslant 1$$

$$\frac{1}{\eta} \geqslant 2$$

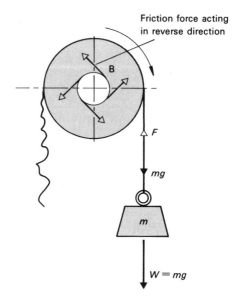

Friction force acting
in reverse direction

B

F

mg

m

W = mg

Fig. 14.23   A simple pulley with the effort removed

That is,

η must be equal to or less than 0.5

Therefore, provided that the frictional forces remain constant (they are actually reduced a little when the effort is removed) when raising and lowering a load a lifting machine of less than 50% mechanical efficiency will not overhaul. This is true of all such machines.

EXERCISE 14 _____

(Assume $g = 9.81 \, \text{m/s}^2$.)

1) In a first-order lever the effort arm is 600 mm and the load arm 60 mm. There is friction at the fulcrum so that in order to raise a load of 1260 N an effort of 140 N must be applied. Find: (a) the mechanical advantage, (b) the velocity ratio, (c) the efficiency of the system.

2) In a second-order lever the effort arm is 800 mm and the load arm is 200 mm. If the efficiency is only 80% because of friction at the pivot find the effort required to raise a load of 1000 N.

3) In a third-order lever the effort arm is 450 mm and the load arm is 1350 mm. The machine has an efficiency of 60%. Find the load that can be raised by an effort of 25 N.

4)   A pulley system of the type shown in Fig. 14.8 has five pulleys. One pulley is used only in order to change the direction of the pull in the free end of the cord. Find: (a) the velocity ratio of the system, (b) the force required to lift a mass of 100 kg if the system is frictionless. Assume the pulleys have negligible mass.

5)   A pulley system of the kind shown in Fig. 14.9 has four pulleys. An effort of 800 N is required to overcome a total load of 2000 N. Calculate: (a) the velocity ratio, (b) the mechanical advantage, (c) the ideal effort, (d) the friction effort, (e) the percentage efficiency of the system.

6)   In a Weston differential block and tackle of the type shown in Fig. 14.11 the larger and smaller diameters of the differential pulley are 300 mm and 280 mm respectively. A pull of 130 N on the 'fall' of the chain will just lift a load weighing 1560 N. (a) Calculate the efficiency of the system. (b) Will the pulley system overhaul?

7)   A simple wheel and axle has a wheel diameter of 300 mm and an axle diameter of 100 mm. When lifting a mass of 70 kg the efficiency of the machine is 85%. Calculate: (a) the mechanical advantage, (b) the velocity ratio, (c) the effort required to raise the 70 kg mass.

8)   The larger and smaller diameters of the axle of a differential wheel and axle are 100 mm and 80 mm respectively. The wheel diameter is 300 mm. Calculate: (a) the velocity ratio of the machine, (b) the mechanical advantage if the efficiency is 85%, (c) the effort required to raise a mass of 250 kg.

9)   (a) Define the terms 'pitch' and 'lead' as applied to a screw thread. (b) A screw jack is operated by applying an effort to the free ends of two cords wrapped around the pulley of the jack as shown in Fig. 14.14. The jack has a two-start thread, the pitch of which is 12 mm. The diameter of the jack pulley is 300 mm. The pull on each of the two cords needs to be 50 N when raising a mass of 300 kg. Determine: (i) the velocity ratio, (ii) the mechanical advantage, (iii) the efficiency, (iv) the ideal effort, (v) the friction effort. (vi) Will the machine overhaul when the effort is removed?

10)   Two spur gear wheels, each one mounted on a shaft, engage one another. Wheel A has 55 teeth and wheel B 330 teeth. Wheel A drives wheel B. Determine: (a) the velocity ratio of the gears, (b) the angular velocity of wheel B in radians/second when wheel A is rotating at 360 rev/min clockwise.

11) Two shafts A and B are connected by spur gear wheels which are mounted and keyed to these shafts. The gear wheels transmit motion through an idler gear wheel mounted on a third shaft C. If the gear wheels on shafts A and B have 60 and 210 teeth respectively and the idler gear has 45 teeth determine: (a) the velocity ratio of the system, (b) the angular velocity of shaft B when shaft A is turning at 420 rad/s anticlockwise and driving shaft B.

12) A worm-and-wheel lifting device of the kind shown in Fig. 14.20 has an effort wheel of 80 mm diameter and a drum diameter of 40 mm. The number of teeth on the wheel is 50 and the worm has a two-start thread. When lifting a load of 250 kg an effort of 80 N is required. Calculate: (a) the velocity ratio, (b) the mechanical advantage, (c) the efficiency. (d) Will the machine overhaul if the effort is removed?

13) A screw jack which has a velocity ratio of 30 gave the following results when put on test.

Load (N)	40	80	120	160	200	240
Effort (N)	2.8	4.6	6.4	8.4	10.1	12.0

Plot the graph relating load and effort and determine: (a) the law of the machine, (b) the efficiency when the load is: (i) 120 N and, (ii) 240 N.

14) A lifting machine which has a velocity ratio of 10 was tested. Loads were applied and the efforts necessary to lift these loads were measured. These values are tabulated below.

Load (N)	0	200	400	650	800	1000	1200	1400
Effort (N)	22	43	67	92.5	108	129	152	173

(a) Calculate the corresponding values of mechanical advantage, efficiency, ideal effort, and friction effort. (b) Tabulate these values together with the load and effort values given above. (c) With load as base, plot the remaining quantities against the load. (d) Determine from the graph the law of the machine.

15) Calculate the limiting efficiency for the machine referred to in question 14.

APPENDIX

SAFETY WITH ELECTRICITY

ELECTRICAL SUPPLIES

As an engineering technician you are likely to come across a variety of electrical supplies and types of electrical equipment. The major kinds of electrical supply are:

(a) 'Domestic' single-phase supply. In the UK this is a.c. and the standard voltage 240 V r.m.s.

(Remember that 'peak' voltage is greater than this.)

(b) Three-phase supply, again a.c. and with a line-voltage value of 415 V r.m.s.

(c) Voltage up to 400 000 V if you are involved in the electrical generation and distribution industry.

(d) Voltage of several kilovolts a.c. or d.c. in various kinds of equipment, e.g. voltage supplies to cathode ray tubes.

(e) High-frequency supply for specialist applications, e.g. diathermy, microwave ovens.

(f) Low-voltage high-current supplies, e.g. d.c. supplies for electroplating.

All the above give rise to *hazards*. The main hazards are:

(i) electrical shock which can lead to death,

(ii) fire,

(iii) tissue burn,

(iv) radiation leading to tissue damage.

People can be protected from these hazards by the correct

• Installation

• Use

• Maintenance

of electrical supplies and equipment.

Safety codes and procedures are laid down to minimise the danger arising from these hazards. As a technician extra care is required since you may have to maintain and repair equipment, and test equipment at work or in the college laboratories. *Remember the safety of others as well as yourself may depend on you.*

In this section we will confine ourselves to shock and fire hazards.

ELECTRIC SHOCK HAZARDS

The effect of an electrical shock on the human body depends on:

(a)   the path a current takes through the body;

(b)   the magnitude of the current;

(c)   the duration of the current;

(d)   the nature of the current — d.c. or a.c. — and frequency.

CURRENT PATH

This will depend on which parts of the body come into contact with the 'live' wire of a supply, and which part is connected to 'earth' — usually some metal which is at earth potential. A path between the hands thus passing through the chest and heart is extremely dangerous (Fig. A1). Such currents will effect the heart and breathing muscles.

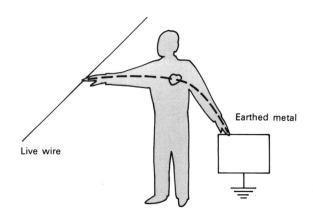

Live wire

Earthed metal

Fig. A1   A highly dangerous current path through the heart

MAGNITUDE OF CURRENT

The magnitude of the current is a critical factor. This will depend on the voltage of the supply touched and the resistance of the path through the body. For example, if your hands are wet or sweaty when a 'live' wire is touched and your feet are on damp ground, the resistance of the path through your body will be much less than if your hands were dry and you were standing on dry timber. In the first case a much smaller voltage could be lethal than in the second case. Remember, 50 V can under certain circumstances be as dangerous as 500 V in other conditions.

A rough guide to the effect of the size of the current is given in Fig. A2.

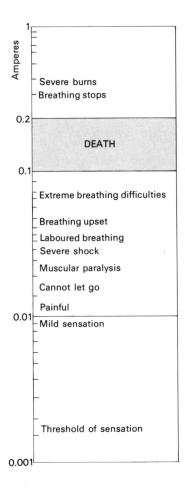

Fig. A2   The effect of an electric current through the human body

Muscular contraction in the human body, be it in your arms, heart or respiratory muscles, works by virtue of small electrical impulses travelling along nerves connected to these muscles. Muscles, therefore, respond to an electric current, and a current resulting from touching a live wire can cause contraction of a muscle. This can be particularly dangerous as the first effect of grasping a 'live' piece of equipment could be contraction of the hand muscles which would make it impossible to 'let go'. In the case of the respiratory muscles, again they can contract and be paralysed thus stopping breathing. For the heart, the constant heart-beat works by a fine balance of electrical impulses along its nerve network. An externally applied current as in a shock disturbs this and the heart can go into fibrillation, and if this happens to the ventricles the heart simply quivers and ceases to pump blood. Lack of blood to the brain for about a minute can result in death, hence *rapid action* is required in the case of shock of this magnitude. Resuscitation procedures are given later.

AVOIDING ELECTRIC SHOCK

- Remember that any electrical supply or equipment can be dangerous.

- Never assume that any 'wire' or 'terminal' is electrically 'dead' until you have checked that it is by either a voltmeter or neon tester.

- Do not stand on a damp floor, lean on walls or on any metal parts when working on electrical equipment.

- Sometimes its a good idea to keep one hand in your pocket – to safeguard connecting yourself across a supply.

- Ensure that any equipment you use is adequately earthed or has double insulation. If in any doubt wear rubber gloves.

- Ensure that the equipment is connected to the supply through standard plugs and sockets or terminals. Be especially wary of 'extension leads'. (See Exercise 15, Question 4, p. 296.)

PROTECTION AGAINST SHOCK

Domestic and industrial electrical equipment and appliances, and electrical supplies, have to conform to certain safety standards. These standards ensure that any 'live' parts are well protected, for example by insulation, and cannot normally be touched.

However, hazards can arise in two ways:

(a)   misuse — such as removal of insulation;

(b)   as a result of wear and tear or deterioration of insulation, the exposed metal parts of an appliance may connect with the live conductor hence making the metal live, e.g. the case of an electric fire becoming alive — highly dangerous.

Protection against (a) is difficult, but can be provided to a certain extent by incorporating earth-leakage circuit-breakers in the a.c. supply. The circuit-breakers detect a small 'leakage' current to earth such as would flow through a human that touches the live supply. This results in the circuit breaker operating and cutting off the supply.

Protection against (b) is afforded by using a three-wire supply at the consumer end — Live (L), Neutral (N) and Earth (E). The system is shown in Fig. A3.

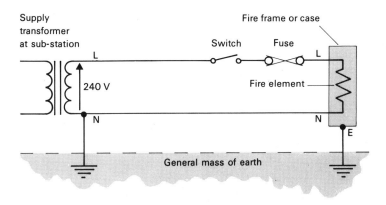

Fig. A3   The live, neutral and earth wire system

One side of the supply transformer secondary is earthed by connecting it to an electrode buried in the earth. This earthed side becomes the *neutral* of the supply. At the consumer end the exposed metal parts of any appliance (e.g. an electric fire) are connected to the *earth* wire of the local supply which is eventually connected to an earth electrode. This often was the water supply when it was metallic pipes, but now with polythene pipes it cannot always be used.

EFFECT OF A FAULT

Danger arises if, from any cause, the live wire touches the exposed metal parts. Fig. A4 shows such a fault. In this case it can be seen there is a 'short circuit' from the live conductor through the 'fault' and the metal parts to earth and back to the transformer neutral. If the resistance of this circuit is low enough, an excessive current will flow through the fuse and it will 'blow' thus breaking the circuit.

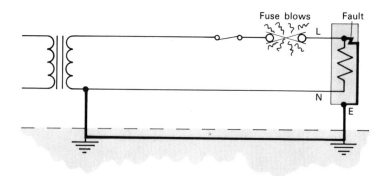

Fig. A4   System blows fuse to prevent exposed metal becoming 'live'

EARTH RESISTANCE PROBLEMS

In the above we have assumed that perfect zero resistance contact can be made to earth at both the sub-station and the consumer end. This is not possible and results in resistance being present at both these points as shown in Fig. A5.

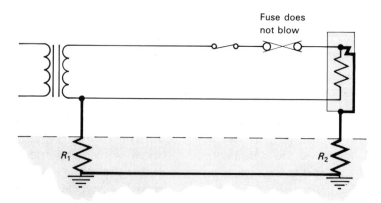

Fig. A5   The effect of earth resistance

The 'fault' current is limited by this resistance, and would be $240\,\text{V} \div (R_1 + R_2)$. It is essential that $(R_1 + R_2)$ is low enough to give a current great enough to 'blow' the fuse — generally at least three times the fuse rating. The major problem generally occurs at the consumer end, and it is necessary to ensure that the effective value of R_2 is low enough.

A simple method of testing for adequate earth protection is to deliberately connect a low value of resistor between L and E and measure the 'earth' current. This can be done by measuring the voltage across the 'fault' resistor. From this information you can work out whether a real direct earth fault will below the fuse.

OTHER SAFETY FACTORS

It should be noted that the switch and fuse are always placed in the live conductor. It is essential, of course, that the fuse is here if protection is to be provided as discussed above.

Having the switch in the live conductor always ensures that when the switch is *off* there is no live voltage on the appliance. Consider the situation if the switch was in the *neutral* line (Fig. A6). The circuit would appear 'dead', but if someone tampered with it, for example replacing a fire element, the live conductor would be touched with disastrous results.

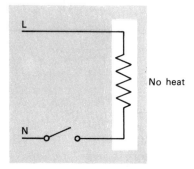

Fig. A6   The danger of a switch in a neutral line. The element is still live

The following colour code is used for single-phase supplies:

LIVE	Brown
NEUTRAL	Blue
EARTH	Green or green and yellow stripes

The correct way to connect these to a 13 A flat pin plug is shown in Fig. A7.

For safety ensure that:

(a)   all leads are securely attached to the terminals and that the insulation is satisfactory up to the point of contact,

(b)   the cable and its outer sheath is securely attached to the plug so that any force from pulling the lead is taken at this point and not on the terminals,

(c)   the fuse rating is suitable for the appliance used.

Fuses are available in 3 A, 5 A, 10 A and 13 A ratings. The current rating can be calculated by dividing the appliance wattage by the supply voltage (generally 240 V in the UK).

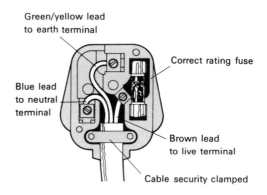

Fig. A7   Connecting a 13 A plug

FIRE HAZARDS

All electrical conductors have a certain resistance. This is kept as low as possible by using materials such as copper. However, at a certain value of current the heat generated may become excessive and the temperature rise sufficient to cause a fire. Thus all cables have a safe *current-carrying capacity* and this should not be exceeded. To safeguard exceeding this value a fuse is incorporated in the circuit, for example, the fuse distribution board near the entry of the supply to a house. The fuse rating is equal to or less than the maximum current rating of the cable, and if the current becomes excessive the fuse will blow.

Thus the fuse protects both against electrical shock and fire hazards.

Circuit-breakers may also be used instead of fuses to limit the current to a safe value. In many ways they are superior to fuses in that they can act more quickly and are not so readily tampered with as, for example, putting the wrong wire size into a fuse.

It should be noted that the heat generated in a cable depends where it is situated. If it is in free air, it will dissipate the heat more readily than in a conduit. For the same reason extension leads should not be used near their maximum ratings when coiled up since the innermost turns will have difficulty in dissipating the heat.

RULES IN THE LABORATORY

During your college course you will be required to carry out experiments on electrical equipment. This will entail assembling circuits and making measurements. Obviously there are some dangers involved, but these can be minimal provided you obey the following:

- Before you connect any circuit to the supply terminals, and before you make any changes to a circuit such as altering connections or adding a meter, *switch off.* You should assure *yourself* that the supply is OFF and not rely on your partner.

- Make sure you know where the *safety devices* are in the laboratory. Most laboratories will have safety *off* buttons that will rapidly turn off the supply. Otherwise, be sure you know where the on/off switch is for your equipment — and make sure it is not out of reach.

- Follow carefully the procedures laid down for the laboratory and make yourself aware of any potential hazards.

- A neat, orderly and methodical approach to your experiments helps safety. Keep your work station clean and free from clutter. All wires should be firmly secured and meters placed where they can be easily read.

- If circuits have to be established from circuit diagrams, the easiest way is to connect the main CURRENT path first and add any parallel branches and voltmeters last. For example, to set up the circuit of Fig. A8(a):

  (a) Determine the main current path. This is shown in black in Fig. A8(b).

  (b) Connect up the above (black) part of the circuit.

  (c) Connect the voltmeter last.

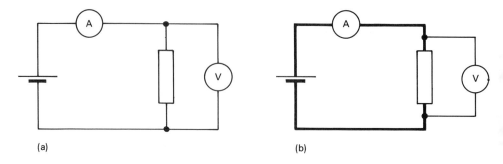

Fig. A8   (a) A simple circuit and (b) its main current path, which should be connected first

- Beware of rotating machinery. Do not wear loose clothes that could be caught in any moving parts.

- Chemical hazards can arise from cleaning solvents, etching chemicals, and acids. Always use suitable protective clothing, gloves, and eye or face protection. Always work in adequately ventilated areas and ensure that chemicals are disposed of safely.

- Do not be distracted when carrying out experiments and be in an alert mental condition (not tired).

FIRST AID FOR ELECTRIC SHOCK

Rapid action is essential, but equally important is to ensure that neither you or your colleagues become a second casualty. So:

- Switch off the offending supply — even if this means shutting down the whole laboratory.

- If the above is not immediately possible, pull the casualty away by holding to his clothes or pushing the equipment away with a dry stick. Avoid at all costs standing on damp or wet ground or using wet hands.

- The patient should be carefully laid on his back and examined quickly. If breathing, make the patient comfortable then tilt the head backwards and ensure the airways are clear. If breathing has stopped, *immediately* apply artificial respiration as detailed in the chart opposite.

ELECTRIC SHOCK | ACT AT ONCE – DELAY IS FATAL

make sure it is safe to approach

If the casualty is not clear of the source of the shock break the contact by switching off the current, removing the plug, or wrenching the cable free. If this is not possible, stand on dry insulating material (rubber, wood, brick, thickly folded newspaper, books) and try to push or pull the casualty clear of the contact using similar insulating material (such as a broomstick) as a lever. Do not touch him with bare hands.

if the casualty is breathing

Place casualty in the recovery position and call medical aid.

recovery position ➡

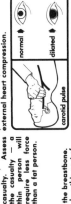

if the casualty is NOT breathing

Get someone to call medical aid while you

start artificial respiration—speed is essential

1. Check airway is not blocked. Remove loose fitting dentures, sweets etc. from the casualty's mouth.

2. Press head well back with one hand and pull the chin up with the other.

3. Take a deep breath. Pinch casualty's nostrils together with your fingers. Seal your lips around his mouth and blow air steadily into his lungs. Watch his chest rise.

4. Remove mouth and watch chest fall.

5. Repeat and continue inflations at your natural rate of breathing.
When casualty starts breathing place him immediately in the recovery position.

if AFTER FOUR INFLATIONS casualty does not respond to artificial respiration

Check carotid pulse, colour of skin and pupils of eyes. If the pulse is absent, the skin bluish-grey and the pupils dilated this means that the casualty's heart has stopped beating.
Give the casualty a decisive thump on the lower part of the breastbone, slightly to the left, with a clenched fist.

Take care! Too small a thump will be ineffective but too large a thump could injure the casualty. Assess the casualty – a thin person will require less force than a fat person.

Check again for the carotid pulse. If the pulse is present continue inflations. When the casualty breathes on his own, place him immediately in the recovery position. If the pulse is still absent start external heart compression.

external heart compression

Feel for the lower half of the breastbone. Place the heel of your hand on this part of the bone, slightly to the left, keeping palm and fingers off the chest. Cover this hand with the heel of the other hand. With arms straight, rock forward, pressing down on the lower half of the breastbone. Do this 15 times — once per second and then give the casualty two inflations.

Check the pulse again. If it is present continue with inflations until casualty breathes on his own, then place him immediately in the recovery position. If the pulse is absent repeat the 15 compressions and two inflations until there is a response from the casualty.

normal ◀ ▶

dilated ◀ ▶

carotid pulse

On recovery continue to watch casualty carefully as breathing may stop. If it does, turn casualty on his back and start artificial respiration again. Cover casualty with one blanket only.

doctor:-	
phone:-	
ambulance:-	
phone:-	
hospital:-	
phone:-	
nearest first aid:-	
phone:-	

Prepared in co-operation with St. John Ambulance.

electrical review
Dorset House, Stamford St., London, SE1 9LU
© IPC Business Press Limited

Fig. A9   Electric shock emergency procedure

ACCIDENT REPORTS

All accidents should be reported, preferably in writing, to your instructor or laboratory supervisor. The following should be included:

- exact circumstances under which accident occurred;
- names of observers or participants in experiment;
- a list of equipment in use including serial numbers;
- any unusual conditions, e.g. water on floor;
- any suggestions as to its cause;
- any suggestions for improved procedures in dealing with such an accident.

EXERCISE 15

1) List the two most likely hazards that can result from using electrical appliances.

2) For a domestic supply what would you expect to happen when a short-circuit is applied between the live and earth outlets at a socket? If nothing happens what is the most likely fault?

3) What would be the most appropriate fuse ratings for the following appliances which are for use on the 240 V a.c. supply: (a) 100 W lamp, (b) 2 kW electric fire; (c) 500 W vacuum cleaner, (d) medium-size electric cooker (estimate the ratings of the oven and hot plates), (e) colour television receiver (estimate its rating).

4) No socket outlet exists where it is wanted to use an electric fire. An extension lead is made up from two-core cable, and inadvertently the live and neutral connections reversed on the socket end of the lead. The lead is connected to an unswitched socket. A person claims that despite the fact that the fire was switched off, he received a shock when he moved it. Explain fully – with diagrams – the circumstance that made this possible.

5) What current flows in: (a) the live conductor, (b) the neutral conductor, and (c) the earth conductor, for a 3 kW immersion heater connected to a 240 V supply? If a short-circuit fault develops between the live and earth of the heater, and if the resistance to earth of the earth conductor is 5 Ω, what current will flow in each of the three conductors under these conditions?

ANSWERS

EXERCISE 1

1) b
2) d
3) c
4) a
5) d (Note that the 15 Ω resistor can be replaced by two 30 Ω resistors in parallel)
6) d (Note comment for answer 5)
7) d
8) a
9) b (since the two resistors in parallel will be effectively less than 1 Ω)
10) b
11) c
12) d
13) a
14) b
15) c (since very little will go through the 100 Ω and the effective resistance of the circuit is just over 10 Ω)
16) 6 Ω
17) 12 Ω
18) 24 V
19) $V = 110$ V, $I = 2$ A
20) The voltage between P and the bottom line should be 9 V, so P should be 9/12 or 3/4 of the way up the resistor.
(a) Yes — it would be impossible to make the voltmeter read zero
(b) No — the situation would be as originally
21) 60 Ω. The voltage across the 200 Ω is $(2/3) \times 12$ V $= 8$ V, hence the voltage across R must be 8 V. ∴ V across the 120 Ω will be 16 V, so R will be one-half of 120 Ω. (Note: it is assumed the voltmeter takes no current)
22) (a) 1.09 A (b) 10.91 V
23) (a) 7.89 V and 10.53 V (b) 21 V
(c) 30 A

EXERCISE 2

1) c
2) a
3) c
4) a
5) b
6) b
7) c
8) b
9) c
10) b
11) a
12) d
13) a
14) (a) 78–82 V (i.e. 80 ± 2% of 100 V)
(b) 76–84 V (i.e. 80 ± 2% of 200 V)
15) (b) (i) 0.5 mA (ii) 25 mA (c) 51 mA
16) (b) (i) 5 V (ii) 10 V
17) For 100 V approximately 1 MΩ
(accurately 1 MΩ − 1000 Ω)
For 25 V approximately 250 000 Ω
(accurately 249 kΩ)
18) A shunt resistance of approximately 0.05 Ω will be required (accurately 50/999 Ω)
19) $R_1 = 0.5$ Ω, $R_2 = 5$ Ω, $R_3 = 55.56$ Ω
(50 mV/0.9 mA)
(Note: R_1 and R_2 values are approximate, and are based on ignoring the current through the meter which in both cases is very much smaller than the current through the shunt)
20) 200 mA (Note that when 10 mA flows through the meter and the 9 Ω resistor the voltage across them is 190 mV which also appears across the 1 Ω resistor)

21) (a) $V_{AB} = 2$ V; $V_{BC} = 10$ V
(b) (i) 1.714 V (ii) 8.571 V
(c) In both cases $V_{AB} : V_{BC}$ is $1 : 5$
(Moral: as long as the same meter is used to measure the voltage across two resistors in series it will always produce the correct ratio despite its 'loading' effect)

22) (a) *in series* with the resistor (to the right side of the motor)
(b) *across* the battery

23) (a) An ammeter in the battery line would measure the current through R_1, and an ammeter in the R_2–R_3 circuit would measure the current through R_3
(b) The voltmeter should be connected *across* R_3

24) Since the voltmeter is connected across the ammeter and motor, the resistance calculated is the effective series resistance of the ammeter and motor. For a more accurate answer the voltmeter should be connected across the motor only

EXERCISE 3

1) b

2) c

3) d

4) d

5) (a)

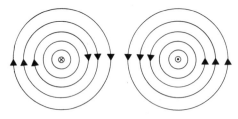

Individual

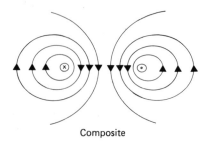

Composite

(b)

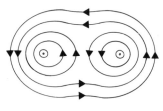

Individual

Composite

6) In (a) the conductors will be repelled from each other, and in (b) attracted to each other.

7) Magnetic field, current and motion.

8) Either use Fleming's left-hand rule or draw the magnetic field due to the current in the conductor and determine the force by superimposing the fields.

9) 0.25 T

10) 4×10^{-5} Wb (from $\Phi = BA$)

11) 8×10^{-3} N (from $F = BLv$) and the force will be upwards.

12) 0.8 V (from $e = BLv$)

13) (a) from left to right   (b) into end D
(c) ends B and C should be connected together

14) (a) Between the intervals of 0–100 ms, 200–300 ms and 400–500 ms
(b) During the first and second of the above
(c) During 400–500 ms

15) At 5 ms and 15 ms (at these moments the flux is not changing)

16) 150 turns

17) (a) Transformer A 1:5 (step-up)
    Transformer B 2:1 (step-down)
    (b) Connect the primary of transformer
    B to the secondary of transformer A
    (c) 2.4 V, by connecting the two as
    'step-down' transformer of 5:1 and
    2:1 giving an overall ratio of 10:1

18)

Column 1	Column 2	Column 3
Equation	Represents	Units
BLI	Force on a conductor	Newton
$\dfrac{V_2}{V_1}$	Turns ratio	None
BA	Magnetic flux	Weber
$N\dfrac{d\Phi}{dt}$	Generated voltage	Volt
$\dfrac{\Phi}{A}$	Flux density	Tesla
BLv	Generated voltage	Volt
$V_1 I_1$	Transformer primary power	Watt

19) (a) (i) A voltage will be generated
    across the ends of the rolling rod.
    This voltage will produce a current
    in the current formed by the rod,
    rails A and B and the ammeter
    (ii) The magnetic field produced by
    current in the rod will interact with
    the 'main' magnetic field
    (b) The current will be from B to A (use
    Fleming's *right-hand* rule)
    (c) The force on rod C will be opposite
    to the direction it is rolling (use
    Fleming's *left-hand* rule)

20) (a) 180 V   (b) 155.9 V

EXERCISE 4

1) 40 ms, 1 ms, 50 μs, 0.2 μs
2) 20 Hz, 500 Hz, 10 KHz, 4 MHz
3) See waveforms at foot of page
4)

Amplitude	B, D
Frequency	1/A, 1/E
Periodic time	A, E
Negative peak value	D
One-half periodic time	C

5) 5 V, 100 Hz

6) Amplitude = $\frac{1}{2} \times 3.8 \times 5 = 9.5$ V.

   Frequency = $\dfrac{1}{4\text{ms}} = 250$ Hz

7) (a) 3000 rev/min (b) 1500 rev/min
   (c) 6000 rev/min

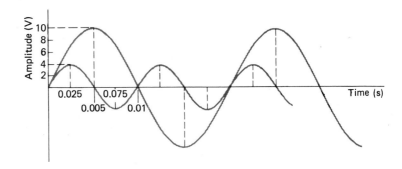

8)

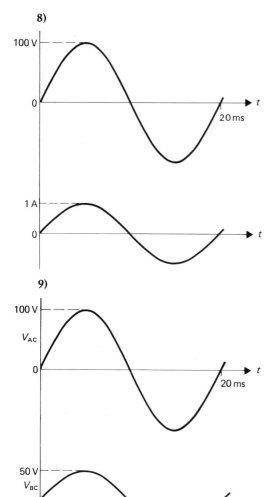

9)

10) (a) 2 A   (b) 200 V
11) (a) 5 A   (b) 505 V
12) 1.41 A, 3.54 A, 21.22 A, 100 A
13) 2.82 A
14) (b) The r.m.s. value of (a) is $25/\sqrt{2}$
    which is less than 24 V in case (b)
15) (b) The 240 V a.c. is the r.m.s. voltage

EXERCISE 5

1) b
2) Intensity (Brilliance) and Focus
3) Y-shift and X-shift

4) Volts/cm
5) Time/cm
6) (a) 3 cm   (b) 0.75 cm. The deflection
   would be downwards when the battery
   is reversed
7) (a) 1 Volt/cm   (b) 1 ms/cm

EXERCISE 6

6) (a) 114 N/mm^2 (b) 0.000622
   (c) 164×10^3 N/m
7) 39.24 mm
8) 80 N/mm^2; 0.000 045
9) (a) 10 000 mm^2 (b) 30.27 mm
10) 35.1 GN/m^2
11) 41.20 mm; 0.87 mm
12) (a) 23 MN/m^2 (b) 0.434 mm
    (c) 1152×10^6 N/m
14) (e) 148 kN   (f) 200 kN   (g) 180 kN
15) (a) 370 MN/m^2 (b) 500 MN/m^2
    (c) 450 MN/m^2
16) (a) 32.8%   (b) 13.3%
17) 200 000 MN/m^2
18) 100 000 MN/m^2
19) 127 MN/m^2
20) 80 MN/m^2; 76.4 MN/m^2
21) 264 kN
22) 78 kN
23) 132 mm
24) (a) 30.9 mm   (b) 26.8 mm
25) 23.4 mm
26) (a) 25 MN/m^2 (b) 500 kN
27) (a) 13 MN/m^2 (b) 1.54 mm^2
28) 200 GN/m^2
29) (a) 250 MN/m^2 (b) 545 MN/m^2
    (c) 25.9%   (d) 61.18%
30) (a) 26%   (b) 74%

EXERCISE 7

1) 70 N at 21°45′ to the horizontal
2) 2598 N; 1500 N
3) 1305 N
4) 40 N; 30 N
5) 4321 N; 1015 N
6) 175 N; 303 N
7) 113 N at 130° to the horizontal
8) $P = 106$ N; $Q = 114$ N
9) 36 N at 120° to the 60 N force
10) 11 kN, 28 kN

EXERCISE 8

1) 40 N; 80 N upwards
2) 2200 N; 2000 N downwards
3) (a) $Q = 8$ N, $R = 24$ N
   (b) $P = 160$ N, $R = 240$ N
   (c) $y = 75$ mm, $R = 175$ N
   (d) $x = 90$ mm, $R = 175$ N
4) $R_A = 1675$ N, $R_C = 4825$ N
5) 2 kN
6) 2.375 kN; 4.525 kN
7) $x = 40$, $y = 6$
8) $R_B = 15.43$ kN; $R_C = 7.57$ kN

EXERCISE 9

1) 25 m
2) 139 s; 1929 m
3) (a) 140 m   (b) 15 m   (c) 177 s
4) (a) $3\frac{1}{3}$ s   (b) 15 m
5) (a) $11\frac{1}{3}$ s   (b) 187 m
6) (a) 0.3 m/s^2 (b) 0.375 m/s^2
   (c) 45 m
7) 6000 rev/min
8) 5.65 m/s
9) 5.77 rad/s^2
10) 1.8π $(= 5.652)$ rad/s^2
11) 10 s
12) (a) 12.5 rad   (b) 5 rad/s
    (c) 1.875 m   (d) 0.75 m/s
13) (a) 55 m/s westwards
    (b) 55 m/s eastwards
14) 2.69 m/s in direction $21°48'$ south
    of east
15) (a) 0 m/s   (b) 6 m/s upwards to the
    right at $60°$ to the horizontal
    (c) 12 m/s horizontally from left to
    right
16) 72 km/h at $123°42'$ to the direction
    in which car R is travelling

EXERCISE 10

1) 0.1 m/s^2
2) 6.7 m/s^2
3) (a) 196.2 N;   (b) 122.6 m
4) 50 kg
5) 489 N

6) 5 N
7) 3153 N
8) 3511 N
9) (a) 788 N   (b) 332 N
10) (a) retarding at 0.65 m/s^2
    (b) moving at uniform speed
    (c) accelerating at 0.65 m/s^2

EXERCISE 11

1) 16 N
2) 0.33
3) 1000 N
4) 91 N;   107.7 N
5) 0.27
6) 0.095
7) 0.4
8) 224 N
9) (a) 2.5 N   (b) 2 N
10) 800 N

EXERCISE 12

1) 706 J
2) 48.6 kJ
3) 2.4 kJ
4) 2.25 kJ
5) 301 J
6) 11.86 kJ
7) 1 kJ
8) 1.56 kJ
9) 1.885 kJ
10) 339 kJ
11) 2.99 kJ
12) 3.53 J
13) 236 J
14) 188.5 kN
15) (a) 90 J   (b) 160 J   (c) 226.9 kJ
16) 1.962 J
17) (a) 800 J   (b) 16.3 m
18) 617 kJ; 6.29 m
19) 22.1 m/s; 1472 J; 14.0 m
20) 26.10 m
21) 6244 kJ
22) 404 kJ
23) 18 056 kJ
24) 32.66 kg
25) 946 J/kg $°$C

26) 30 100 kJ
27) 12 074 kJ
28) 475 MJ
29) 23.05 °C
30) 34.06 °C
31) 27.47 °C
32) 1043 J/kg °C
33) 28 475 kJ
34) 191 845 kJ
35) 429.05 kJ
36) 806.2 kJ
37) 9026 MJ
38) 2.271 km/s

EXERCISE 13

1) 0.000 016 per °C
2) 120.551 mm
3) 12.053 m
4) 200 °C
5) 25.22 m
6) 719 °C
7) 1.9996 m
8) (a) 103.5 °C   (b) 1000.92 mm
9) 1035 mm^3
10) 2.6 cm
11) 48.00 cm
12) (a) 0.051 84 cm^3 (b) 0.045 36 cm^3
13) 3794 mm^3
14) 12.755 cm^3; 0.000 196 per °C;
    0.000 169 per °C

EXERCISE 14

1) (a) 9   (b) 10   (c) 0.9
2) 312.5 N
3) 5 N
4) (a) 16   (b) 61.31 N

5) (a) 4   (b) 2.5   (c) 500 N
   (d) 300 N   (e) 62.5%
6) (a) 0.4   (b) No
7) (a) 2.55   (b) 3   (c) 269.3 N
8) (a) 30   (b) 25.5   (c) 96.2 N
9) (b) (i) 39.28 (ii) 29.43 (iii) 74.92%
   (iv) 74.92 N (v) 25.08 N (vi) Yes
10) (a) 6   (b) 2π or 6.28 rad/s
    anticlockwise
11) (a) 3.5   (b) 120 rad/s anticlockwise
12) (a) 50   (b) 30.6   (c) 0.61   (d) Yes
13) (a) $E = 0.046\,W + 1$
    (b) (i) 62.5% (ii) 66.66%
14) (d) $E = 0.108\,W + 22$
15) 92.6%

EXERCISE 15

1) Electric shock and fire
2) The fuse would blow. If nothing happens
   there is likely to be an inadequate earth
   at the consumer end
3) (a) 3 A   (b) 13 A   (c) 5 A   (d) 30 A
   (e) 3 A
4) Your diagram should indicate that the
   'live' wire comes through direct to the
   element of the fire instead of via the
   switch. A shock could have been produced either by touching the 'element'
   although it was not on, or due to a
   'short' between the 'neutral' end of the
   element and the fire case – which would
   not necessarily show when the fire was
   connected correctly to a 3-pin socket
5) (a) and (b) 12.5 A   (c) zero
   With a fault as indicated 48 A (240/5)
   would flow from the live conductor,
   through the fault and in the earth wire,
   in addition to the previous normal
   currents

INDEX